The Smallest Tadpole's War
in the
Land of Mysterious Waters

Diane Swearingen

The Smallest Tadpole's War in the Land of Mysterious Waters

Cover design by Charity Myers

THE SMALLEST TADPOLE'S WAR IN THE LAND OF MYSTERIOUS WATERS is based on a true story. It started as a biography, a family story, and ended with a love of Florida history.

ISBN: 978-0-692-50974-6

The Smallest Tadpole's War

in the Land of Mysterious Waters

is part of the

Florida Special Collection

at the

State Library of Florida

University of Florida Smathers Library

Florida State University Strozier Library

Gulf Coast State College

Florida State University Goldstein Library

catalogs it as

Juvenile Literature

Dedication

This book is dedicated to my family and the families of American soldiers who answer the call to duty, keeping us free.

Acknowledgments

Thank you to the State Archives of Florida, the *Florida Times-Union* and Henry's angels:

Dr. Sharon Hartman
Adrian Fogelin
Gina Hogan Edwards

A special thank you, also, to my OLLI (Osher Lifelong Learning Institute) writing teacher, Heather Whitaker.

"A kind, gentle and engaging read—that also quietly teaches history."

~ Adrian Fogelin

Author of eight novels for middle-grade and young adult readers, she has won numerous awards including two Florida Book Award gold medals.

"This book was an awesome read. I loved the letters, a great way to teach history."

~ Lenita J. Joe

A military wife and retired educator with 45 years of experience, she was twice elected as her school's Teacher of the Year and received the Glenn-Howell educator of the year award in 2005 and again in 2008. She continues to make significant contributions to community education.

Contents

Prologue

It's best I tell their story. Their story is my story, our lives woven together by the threads of history. When Thomas married Louise in 1855, he adopted me and we became a family, sharing the stories that shaped us, stories that would be told and retold the way families do.

At eleven, I became the man of the house when Thomas, a Lieutenant in the 3rd Florida Infantry, left to rendezvous with the Western Army of the Confederacy. I was at his side when we defended Tallahassee at the Battle of Natural Bridge, driving back the Union troops, saving Tallahassee and making it the only unoccupied capital in the Confederacy. I watched Thomas climb the steps of the Florida Capitol, as a Representative and a Senator.

Thomas would tell me, "Henry, I believe the measure of a man is how he answers when duty calls." The Florida Constitution in 1885 was his proudest achievement, his salvation. Serving as

1

President *pro tem* of the Florida Senate in 1891 was his last call to duty.

My favorite book when I was growing up was Thomas's diary. It inspired me to learn to read. Like a pirate who found a buried chest, I couldn't wait to discover the treasure it held.

I have recited every story in my mind a hundred times over to keep their voices from fading. This tale is mine to tell.

I heard the Capitol had been remodeled in 1902 and I took my grandson to see it. We were traveling on the St. Augustine Road just about sunset when we saw a glow. The Capitol had a new dome that glistened in the setting sun. As we got closer, we saw the added wings.

I walked the boy past the Mountain Howitzers that had guarded the entrance for more than fifty years and up the grand staircase. We saw the cupola from the inside and noticed the indoor plumbing. I never dreamed I would see so many changes.

I knew it was time then to honor my promise, time for me to start writing. I am one of the only ones left who can remember the early days, the days when Florida was just a "tadpole" and so was I.

1 Dooly County, Georgia

Thomas and Dooly County, Georgia, start my story. Thomas is both the beginning and the end.

I remember Dooly County in the 1800s like it was yesterday, the red clay roads, the smell of the fresh-turned fields ready for planting, and the pine trees so tall they were just a stretch from touching heaven. Dooly County was created by the Georgia General Assembly in 1821 from land ceded by the Creek Nation. Most people think of Georgia before the Civil War as a place filled with elegant plantations. The counties to the north and east were known for their columned mansions and tree-lined drives. Dooly County is and has always been a rural county, the houses modest and the churches the center of community life. In fact, you

3

never could go far without passing a church. The county only has a few small towns. They are the heart of the county. The Flint River is its backbone.

Thomas's father was a farmer. As farm families do everywhere, he and his family worked their land from "can to can't." They were considered lucky because they owned their own land, but there was little money to go around. Thomas grew up picking anything the family could grow, mostly cotton, corn, and peas.

Thomas had eight brothers and sisters. The older children left school to help with the farm and care for the younger ones. With their help, the family prospered, making it possible for Thomas and Milton, the younger siblings, to stay in school longer than most of the other boys from poor families. The truth was the older boys had been happy to leave school. They spent their days dreaming about fishing the many streams that flowed throughout the county and into the mighty Flint River.

School never came easy to me. Thomas and Louise both loved learning, so I must have been a disappointment. Thomas was the kind of student I always wanted to be. He enjoyed arithmetic and had handwriting that pleased his teachers. Reading was, by far, his favorite subject.

Annie Miller had been the county teacher for years. Thomas was one of her top students when his father decided Thomas already had enough education to handle the needs of the farm. "Time he learned by doing." But Thomas's mother wanted to give her young son the best education possible. Her chance came when two lonely souls united.

Annie was spending the summer with her cousin in Atlanta when she met Catherine Brooks, a neighbor. Catherine's father was a judge and she had been given a private education of exceptional quality. Catherine was well read and had a deep love of poetry. Annie had a basic education, but a thirst for knowledge. The two spent the afternoons reading from Catherine's extensive library, sipping tea and enjoying the friendship of kindred spirits.

During the school year, they wrote to each other and became devoted friends. Catherine's father died shortly before Christmas, leaving her his home and properties. Catherine wrote to Annie, inviting her to come live in the large, now lonely, home.

Years later, Thomas and his classmates found the letter that Annie wrote back to Catherine, tucked away in a poetry book.

March 21, 1841

My Dearest Catherine,

I regret I cannot accept your kind invitation. I care for my mother and could never leave my students.

I have a small but tidy home and would welcome you with all my heart.

Your devoted friend,

Annie

Catherine sold her stately Atlanta home and moved to Dooly.

When Catherine arrived, she had a wagon loaded with nothing but books. It was the talk of the county. Nobody in Dooly County had ever seen so many books.

The two women asked the county to sponsor a second teacher but they were hesitant. Catherine didn't need the small salary, so she urged the county to renovate the schoolhouse instead. She was persistent in the way teachers can be; the county had no choice but to agree.

A storage closet was opened up and a porch enclosed. A partial wall divided the schoolhouse into two rooms. The rooms shared the woodstove in the front and a coatroom in the back with hooks to hold coats and lunch pails. Each of the women used their side of the wall to display great works. Annie's wall was decorated with perfect spelling tests, her students' best handwriting and their art. Catherine's wall was lined with Homer, Keats, and Shakespeare.

Word spread that Catherine Brooks would offer an education usually reserved for the privileged. Everybody who was anybody wanted to include their children in Miss Brooks's classroom, Thomas's mother was among them. She was strongminded when it came to her children. Although she knew her husband had decided Thomas would stay on the farm, she still asked her daughter and son-in-law to take her to the schoolhouse before the end of the school year.

She spoke to Miss Miller about her desire to keep Thomas in school. Annie Miller loved all of her students and was very pleased at the prospect of Thomas returning.

Catherine didn't have Annie's warm nature, and she wasn't sure about Thomas. "Thomas, his brother, and that Marsh boy run around like wild Indians at recess, I can't lend one of my books to that rough boy with those dirty hands."

Annie reminded her, "Running around, making noise, and a little dirt are part of being a boy. Thomas is polite and I feel sure he would be a good choice for your class. His mother is willing to be responsible for the book. She will see to it that his hands are clean."

In the end, Catherine trusted Annie's judgment and agreed to lend Thomas's mother a copy of *Gulliver's Travels.*

One rainy June night, Thomas's mother and one of his sisters were shelling butter beans and his father was whittling on a piece of wood, his hobby. The youngest brother, Milton was curled up with the family dog, enjoying the peace. Thomas was gazing out at the night, watching the rain turn the Georgia clay into a "red sea." He was caught in the rhythm of the rain, when his mother asked him to read. Thomas sat by the lantern and began to read *Gulliver's Travels.* Maybe it was the rain that had given them the gift of time, or the magic spun by an ageless story, but the family listened intently. They were surprisingly patient when Thomas needed to sound out a word. What the word meant was determined by a group discussion, pulling the family deeper into the tale.

By the time the rain ended and the frogs began their chorus, the family was captivated, burning the lantern later than Thomas could remember.

When Thomas returned in the fall, he had just turned twelve. Miss Miller took him by the hand and led him to Miss Brooks, leaving his brother Milton and his best friend Sam Marsh behind in Miss

Miller's class. At first, Miss Brooks was reluctant to welcome Thomas, but when he returned her book in good condition, she seemed pleased.

Miss Brooks required her students to write in a diary each day. Thomas's diary pages were yellow and had the smell of age when I read them, but I loved the stories they told.

August 30, 1843

Dear Diary,

Miss Brooks told me to take a seat. There was an open seat on the front bench. I knew why no one had chosen to sit there. Perched on the other end of the bench was Darby Dunne, "the pincher." Darby's vise-like fingers are known to leave terrible purple bruises. I was feeling lost when Sam's big sister Louise called out to me. She squeezed over and said, "I have room, Thomas. Come sit by me."

The Marsh farm is only one farm over from ours. Louise has always looked after her brother, and Milton and me. We don't always want her help, but she tries her best to keep us out of trouble and out of harm.

Sam says Louise wants to be a teacher. She should be a good one. She holds the babies at church. The women say Louise can soothe the fussiest one and even get them to smile. She made me smile today.

The two families were members of the same church. Thomas, Milton, and Sam always sat together and their families often shared a table on first Sunday.

Their church held an annual Christmas Nativity.

December 20, 1843

Dear Diary,

For as long as I can remember, Louise has been an angel in the Christmas Celebration. This year, she was chosen to be the angel that appeared to the wise men. Sam and I were shepherds in the past, but not this year. We were banned when one of the Sunday school teachers caught us with spit balls.

The air was cool and crisp. The night sky was clear and the stars seemed especially bright. The women each brought a dessert to share after the play and the table was loaded with cookies, cakes, and pies that made my mouth water.

Louise wore a halo, a piece of gold ribbon tied around her head. She wore a long, white robe and her mother had used strips of cloth to roll her hair into curls. Louise reached out to the heavens as she told the wise men to "Follow the Star."

There was more to that story. At the end of the play, Thomas told Sam, "I think your sister is an angel."

Sam said, "Yeah, she is every year."

Sam hadn't understood, but I knew what Thomas meant.

It is hard to say which diary story is my favorite, the first one when Louise saved Thomas or the next entries when Thomas saved Louise.

Miss Brooks always released her students before Miss Miller. Louise and Thomas waited in front of the school for their brothers to be dismissed. The four of them walked side-by-side along the red clay roads until Thomas and Milton turned off just before the Marsh farm.

October 29, 1844

Dear Diary,

The weather was especially hot today. The four of us talked about the Thanksgiving play Miss Miller's class was planning, and we were slowly making our way home in the Georgia heat when we first saw the two strangers. From the start, we avoided looking at the men and walked closer together. I was pretty sure the two men were bounty hunters, hunting for runaway slaves. Sometimes a slave on the run will find safety in our woods.

The Flint River offers direction to those on the run.

We knew to stay clear. Slave hunters are considered by my parents to be an "unsavory group." From the looks of these two, they are the lowest of the low. The older man had a long straggly beard matted with tobacco spit. The younger man had a huge grin on his face that makes him look 'not right in the head.'

When the wind shifted our way, their smell was so bad it could offend a barnyard animal, and the horses they rode had ribs showing. Louise took Milton and Sam by the hand, hurrying them along. When I looked over my shoulder they were leaning back in their saddles, watching us.

Over the years, when Thomas told the story, he would add that the sheriff had learned the bounty hunters were tracking a slave who turned out to be more than they had bargained for, smarter and faster. When he drowned the hound the two had used to track him, they had turned back.

I guess they didn't want to go home empty-handed.

October 30, 1844

Dear Diary,

The heat had Louise and me waiting in the shade of one of the sprawling oaks that surrounded the school. We had only been there a minute or two when we saw the same two riders. Alarm shot through every part of me. The younger man suddenly charged at us, using his foot to knock me to the ground before he rode ahead to serve as a lookout. The older rider grabbed Louise by the arm, pulling her across his saddle.

He was struggling to get a good hold on her when I sprang at him. I grabbed on for dear life. I wrapped my hand in his scraggly beard, clawing and biting as hard as I could. The man loosened his grip on Louise, using one hand to hold her and the other to pound me. Louise slipped from the saddle. She kept struggling, but the man held her arm, straining her shoulder, dragging her along. Before he knocked me back to the ground, I could hear Sam and Milton yelling.

When the two came out of the schoolhouse, they saw the commotion and screamed at the top of their lungs. Both boys ran forward, grabbing rocks to hurl at the kidnappers.

Some of the older boys from Miss Brooks's class rode their horses to school and had stopped to discuss a horse race when they heard Sam's and Milton's calls for help. They charged back just as the man freed Louise and used both fists to drive me to the ground. The lookout rider started back to help his friend, but when he saw Clayton Bradford, Jackson

Bradford, and Joshua Perry racing to the scene, he turned tail and ran.

By then, the whole school was running to our aid. The older man was faced with the hail of rocks Sam and Milton were throwing, three approaching riders, the teachers and a dozen classmates all racing to us. He looked down at Louise and spit a nasty stream of tobacco juice at me before he followed his friend.

Louise and I lay in the dirt. Louise's shoulder was surely dislocated, my eye was swelling, my lip bleeding. Sam and Milton helped us up and, within minutes, we were surrounded by the teachers and our classmates. Dust from the scrimmage still hung in the air.

Everyone is giving me the credit for the rescue, but the truth is, it took the whole school to save Louise.

2   Hero

Whether he deserved it or not, Thomas got the credit for the rescue. It didn't take long for the story to spread. Thomas didn't know what to do with all of the attention.

Miss Brooks and Miss Miller came to the farm to see Thomas. Annie Miller hugged him while Miss Brooks talked to his mother, saying she had a lot to learn about being a teacher. She asked to be forgiven for her "hesitations." Thomas's mother told Catherine she had no doubt Heaven had a hand in bringing her here and how she and Annie Miller were "a true blessing."

When Simon Marsh came by to see Thomas and his father, he was visibly shaken. He paced back and forth as he spoke. "Men like that are an abomination. I heard they brought in a slave woman for bounty. She couldn't stand up they put so much wear on her."

He hung his head before he said, "The sheriff told me a banker's daughter was missing in McRae. She just disappeared out of her yard. After today, there's no doubt those devils had a hand in that. Those two are no more than rabid dogs and should be shot on sight. I don't want to imagine our girl with men like that. Rachel and I can't tell you how grateful we are."

Mr. Marsh shook Thomas's hand. Then he gave him news that changed his joy to sorrow. Louise would not return to school. Simon and Rachel Marsh had decided their daughter had enough education.

On Sunday, the entire congregation of the tiny church wanted to shake Thomas's hand or give him a hug. When the Marsh family arrived, Louise, with her arm in a sling, ran to Thomas. "I love you Thomas," was all she said before she went to the group of girls waiting for her.

November 26, 1844

Dear Diary,

At school I am treated as a hero. Clayton and Jackson Bradford have always been friendly, but now my friendship with the younger brother has grown. Jackson can make a fencepost laugh. He has a pleasant nature and a quick wit. Jackson can impersonate anyone in the class. His impersonation of Miss Brooks leaves me howling with laughter.

Clayton and Jackson both have quality horses and love to race. Clayton is definitely fast, but Jackson rides a horse named Lightning that is as fast as his namesake. Jackson almost never loses. I am there to cheer him and always a part of the celebration that follows.

Books sealed my friendship with Jackson. We both love to read. We compete for Miss Brooks's treasures and talk about the characters like they are our classmates or neighbors. When we share a novel, we use the story clues like a competition for predicting the outcome. We challenge each other to memorize poems. We keep score, laughing and teasing when one of us misses a line. I can't wait to get to school each day.

3   Jackson

Lake Blackshear was formed when a line of islands split the Flint River into channels. I knew Clayton Bradford as "Uncle Clayton." He used to take me fishing at the lake.

Usually, I was more interested in chasing the dragonflies than sitting still to fish. I found the worms fascinating. We brought worms for bait but ended up using flies instead. My uncle and the other fishermen would swat the yellow flies or horseflies that loved the water's edge. The ones that fell were quickly grabbed and placed on a hook. A hook baited with a fly most always caught a fish.

On one trip, Uncle Clayton took me to a spot not far from where his brother lost his life. Fishermen had talked about the drowning for years. I heard the story for the first time while I splashed my feet in the cool water, the Georgia sun on my face.

Uncle Clayton told the others as we fished, "There were five of us camped at the edge of the lake. We were having a great time telling old stories and sharing jokes. Jackson shared a few of his impersonations. When he mimicked our preacher's walk, he had it down so completely, we laughed until our sides hurt."

Uncle Clayton paused to take my catch off the line. I caught a tiny bream, too small to be a keeper. He continued after my hook was ready. "At daylight, we all canoed to the island we called the 'turkey roost.' Each of us made our kill and canoed back to rest up for the barbeque. It was lunchtime when Joshua and I first noticed Jackson wasn't back. We didn't worry. Jackson was strong and a great swimmer, but there was no sign of him or his canoe. We joked that he had fallen asleep or made so much noise he chased all the wildlife away."

Uncle Clayton said it was late afternoon before the group became truly alarmed and started to search. They told some fishermen and, within hours, it seemed everyone in the county was at the lake. The search went on until the sun was setting and the light shone on the lake at the right angle, exposing Jackson's body just below the surface. His upturned canoe was found miles away.

Uncle Clayton could only guess at what had happened, but he lost his brother, and everyone agreed that Dooly County lost one of its favorite sons. Thomas wrote about the loss.

December 2, 1845

Dear Diary,

I was invited to go hunting with some classmates. Since the rescue, I am always invited. Jackson asked if I was coming but I had to tell him I hadn't finished my chores and couldn't join them. Jackson teased, "You move like molasses." My heart aches so much I can't say. I feel like I needed to be there, I should have been there for him.

4 Clayton

Jackson's death was a terrible loss for everyone. Jackson's mother, Sarah Bradford, was devastated. Sarah was family, although I didn't spend much time with her. She attended church faithfully and was known as the best example of a wife and mother. If she had sin, it was one of pride, pride in her family. Sarah delivered three daughters and three fine sons. Her oldest son, Will, was such a strong, healthy baby. She could not believe measles could take him before his first steps. By all accounts, Jackson's death was almost more than she could bear.

At the funeral, Sarah was surrounded by her daughters. She was held up by her husband and Clayton. After the service, Sarah told those close, "Clayton is my hope for the Bradford name. It is up to him now."

The whole county was in mourning when the little church that Thomas and Louise attended held its annual Christmas play. After years of being an angel in the Nativity, Louise was asked to be "Mary" that year. She was a natural choice. Her kind nature and lovely smile caught the attention of many.

February 12, 1846

Dear Diary,

Clayton has started to attend our church. Everyone knows why. He tells anyone who listens, "Louise is the prettiest girl in the county." After church, Clayton and Louise ride in his new buggy or join his family for a picnic. The Bradford family is clearing a home site. Sam and I are sure Clayton is going to propose soon.

When William and Sarah Bradford invited the Marsh family to their church for first Sunday, the whole county knew a marriage would follow.

Joshua Perry would be Clayton's best man, but Clayton came to Thomas and asked him to stand with them. It was an honor, but one that brought mixed feelings.

The wedding of Louise Marsh and Clayton Bradford was the talk of the county. The union of two young people with so much promise made the wedding the event of the year. The June wedding was held at the Bradford family church. It was larger and could accommodate the number of guests.

The church was adorned with every available hydrangea the county had to offer. They were mostly white or soft pink, but they were framed by their deep blue cousins, creating beautiful arrangements. Louise wore her grandmother's ivory gown with a lace bodice. The fit highlighted Louise's tiny waist. The photograph of the wedding was one of the first photographs seen in Dooly County. The bride and groom glowed with happiness.

Thomas stood proudly at the ceremony. He wished Clayton and Louise a wonderful life together. He meant it from the bottom of his heart, but he couldn't wait to be away.

5   Cotton

Nowhere on Earth grows cotton better than South Georgia. Farmers used the Flint River to transport their crop. In the 1800s, rivers were the main means of transportation. The Flint River took its name from the mineral flint, a quartz-based rock found along its bank.

Flint was used to make arrowheads. More than three hundred years ago, a Creek Indian village existed about a day's ride south of Dooly County on the Flint River near Albany. The name of the village was "Thronateeska," their word for "flint picking up place."

Collecting arrowheads was a common hobby along the river. There wasn't a boy who grew up along the Flint that didn't have a few arrowheads to show for it. I had my own collection.

The Flint River is three hundred forty-four miles long and flows across Georgia from its headwaters at southeastern Atlanta to its junction with the Chattahoochee River in southwest Georgia. The

Apalachicola River is formed at the confluence of the Chattahoochee and the Flint rivers, providing access to the coast.

Cost and time made it unrealistic for most farmers to take their cotton crop to market. They generally hired an agent at a fee less than they would spend taking the crop themselves. The agent would collect the bales of waiting cotton and transport them to market. Agents with warehouses near the rivers could store the bales until the riverboats made their pickups. Cotton gins located near the warehouses had an advantage.

Thomas's family and their neighbors delivered their cotton to a landing on the Flint River just below the "turkey roost." They would use the cotton gin to process their crop and sell the baled cotton to an agent. Their agent would ship the cotton to a port at Apalachicola or Bainbridge. From there, it could be shipped to a number of markets.

A cotton gin works by separating the cotton bolls from the usable cotton. The cotton is pulled through a screen by a series of wire teeth driven by gears moved by hand, water, or mule, leaving behind seeds and hulls. The undamaged seeds are used to plant the next crop. Over time, the wire teeth need to be replaced, and the screen cleaned or changed out.

When Thomas and his father arrived just after daybreak in late November 1847, the gin was out of order. What the agents paid the farmer was dependent on the number of processed bales. The needed repairs caused the farmers to wait at the landing for the parts to arrive.

When I read Thomas's diary, I could almost see the steamer coming to collect the cotton.

November 29, 1847

Dear Diary,

I was looking out at the river when the steamer Flint came into sight. I was immediately impressed with her beauty.

While we waited for the gin to be repaired, I learned the Flint was built in Apalachicola and named for the river she was designed to serve. Built in 1846, she has the shine of a new vessel.

The Flint is a stern-wheeler, 83 feet long and 16 feet wide. She was created with a shallow draw to navigate the unpredictable river, but at only 11 horsepower, the Flint is reportedly slow against the current.

Sam Henry Warner, a man who made his living setting up and repairing cotton gins throughout Georgia, was on board that day. He arrived on the *Flint* with the parts needed for the repairs. Unfortunately, he also arrived with his foot heavily bandaged. Sam Henry proceeded to take the old gin apart, replacing parts as he went.

The injured foot cost Sam Henry valuable time. It was an effort for him to bring his tools to and from the steamer. By mid-morning, Thomas was running errands for him and by afternoon, he was helping with the repairs.

When they finished, Sam Henry talked to Thomas's father. Sam Henry told him that Thomas was a fine boy. He thanked them both for the help and went on about the time and pain Thomas had saved him. He said he had three boys and looked forward to the day they would be old enough to be "that kind of help."

The two men shook hands and stood around talking about the quality of the cotton crop and the price it would bring. Thomas's father had watched while Sam Henry talked to Thomas about every step of the cotton gin process. I know his father was a practical man; all farmers are. Thomas would be a great help on the farm, but he had seen that Thomas was fascinated by the shiny new steamer. To Thomas's complete surprise, his father shook hands with Sam Henry again and agreed to allow Thomas to go with him.

Just like that, Sam Henry Warner had hired a new apprentice. When the gin was operational again, and the cotton was ginned, baled, and loaded aboard the *Flint*, it cast off with Thomas aboard. It was the start of what he called his "odyssey."

Reading about his first time aboard the *Flint*, I could almost hear the excitement in his voice.

November 30, 1847

Dear Diary,

When the Flint cast off, there was a banjo player strolling around the decks entertaining passengers and collecting tips. Her rails were lined with excited children, beautiful women, and well-dressed gentlemen. The giant paddle wheel churned the river, producing a steady, soothing sound I loved immediately. I waved to my father until we were completely out of sight.

I was jittery with excitement when Sam Henry called me over to lay down his rules. "I do not tolerate cursing, drunkenness, or gambling. I know you are young, but it is best you be warned to avoid the women that make their living from the men traveling up and down these rivers."

I could always get Thomas to talk about the rivers; he loved the travel. He could talk forever about the food, the scenic beauty of the riverbanks, the people, even the dangers.

January 14, 1848

Dear Diary,

The rivers can be treacherous. We narrowly missed the hull of a burned out vessel today. The ribs of the sunken steamer were barely visible beneath the river's surface.

Fire is always a danger to vessels fueled by wood or coal. The river bottoms are ripe with rocks, fallen trees, and the "bones" of unfortunate riverboats that pose a hidden danger to those that follow.

Sam Henry and Thomas traveled to cotton gins throughout Georgia and Alabama on a number of steamers, but Thomas's favorite was the *Eufaula*.

March 9, 1848

Dear Diary,

It seems Sam Henry and I spend our lives on the river. I have traveled on the Flint, the Edwin Forest, the Ben Franklin, and the Eufaula. The Flint, with barely 4 miles an hour against the current, is the slowest steamer on the river. The Edwin Forest is by far the fastest. She is 93 feet long and has a draw of about 2 feet. The Edwin Forest was designed to tow barges on the Chattahoochee River.

The steamer Ben Franklin has a shallow draw and is famous on the upper reaches of the river for making the trip between Eufaula and Apalachicola "as long as the bottom of the river is moist."

The Eufaula has three times the capacity of the Flint but is not much faster. She has the finest food and entertainment. They say she is famous for the drink and gambling offered. Those who travel on the Eufaula never fail to mention the Alabama beauties that accompany her.

I loved hearing about the rivers. I wanted to know everything. I would beg to hear the tales. When we fished, he would tell his stories, gazing out at the water, remembering. I would picture them in my mind as I listened.

April 3, 1848

Dear Diary,

I am particularly fascinated by the cotton agents we meet on our journeys. They are educated men who have traveled widely. They take the cotton from the farmer to the markets in the north or even across the sea. They talk about ports with ships that would dwarf the Flint or the Eufaula, and vessels faster than the Edwin Forest. They talk about sailing the ocean and describe wonders I can only imagine.

John Hawkes was the agent that Thomas respected and liked most. Hawkes had been born in England. He worked for a trading company based in Liverpool. Hawkes traveled the Chattahoochee River, purchasing the cotton he would ship from Apalachicola to ports in Boston, Savannah, or Liverpool.

April 20, 1848

Dear Diary,

John Hawkes and I were boarding the Ben Franklin when a slave dropped a crate. Everyone on deck heard the sound of broken glass, followed swiftly by the slave's scream as the bullwhip hit his flesh. The slave was beaten without mercy. It seemed everyone around was frozen in place as the injured man, now on the ground, was still feeling the sting of the whip. John Hawkes crossed the deck and grabbed the hand that held the whip, putting a halt to the beating. The man with the whip had a reddish face, but now it was scarlet. He shouted at Hawkes, "Mind your own business." The two struggled as Hawkes held tight.

Hawkes calmly explained, "The violence is offending the women and children and must be stopped." The Captain arrived and shouted orders at the other slaves to move the injured man off the dock. When the red-faced man began to curse, the Captain grabbed the whip and threw it far out into the river.

The beating was the main topic of discussion with a broad range of responses. Many were offended by the action, but few would express support for the foreigner. Thomas was raised in a slave state but had never witnessed such brutality. He made a point to speak to Hawkes. Thomas started with small talk, the weather and the crops, but Hawkes must have been able to tell that Thomas was shaken by the event. Their conversation lasted late into the afternoon. When Hawkes learned Thomas shared his love for poetry, their friendship blossomed.

May 5, 1849

Dear Diary,

After I spent some time with John Hawkes, I asked him, "How did you end up so far from home?" Hawkes walked to the rail overlooking the river as he told me his story. "I came to America to work for my uncle in Savannah. His business was thriving, and he invited me to join him. When I first arrived, I loved Savannah. The parties seemed out of a dream. As time went on, I saw below the surface."

Hawkes and I paused as we spotted a large buck along the riverbank. He continued as the animal melted into the woods. "One night after a recent squabble with a lady friend, I overindulged in liquor and proceeded to tell the Savannah dandies around me what I really thought of them. They go on about demanding respect. I finally had enough and asked one what he had accomplished to earn respect. The landed gentry have idle time on their hands. Savannah should be a renaissance of culture."

Hawkes shifted his weight on the rail as he and I watched a fisherman land his catch. "There should be symphonies, great masterpieces of art and literature. Instead, the fools use their idle time for the Devil's work. Slavery erodes the soul of a slave and that of the master. They just can't see it," he said. "I let them know that as long as there is slavery in the South, they will remain little more than a colony to the North, supplying raw material at a cheap price. My uncle's face turned crimson with embarrassment and he banished me to this route the next day."

I told him, "Idle time was never a problem at our house." We both laughed then stood quietly watching the river banks, lost in our thoughts.

Thomas traveled with Sam Henry for over two years when one door closed and another opened.

May 30, 1850

Dear Diary,

Sam Henry and I have been traveling for days on the Eufaula. I was watching the sunset on the river last night when he came to me with bad news. "Thomas, I hate to tell you this. I want you to know you have been a good worker and this doesn't have anything to do with you or your work. My oldest boy is ready to be an apprentice. I will be picking the boy up at the end of the month. I'm sorry. I wish I could use both of you." My throat tightened. I don't want to leave the river. Dooly County holds my past but no promise for the future.

The sun had almost set that day and the sound of the paddlewheel had Thomas lost in thought, worried about the future, when John Hawkes approached him. Hawkes invited Thomas to dine with him the following evening.

Repairing and maintaining cotton gins was a decent living, but the price of travel had to be deducted from any profit. Sam Henry and Thomas took most of their meals with the crew or in their cabins, but on this night, Thomas polished his boots and joined Hawkes.

June 1, 1850

Dear Diary,

The smell of prime roast beef wafted through the air as we entered the dining room. The room glowed with candlelight. Each table was covered with linen, china, and silver that sparkled. A woman in a velvet dress played a harp and sang softly. I was reminded of a saying my mother used, "Heaven had a hand in this."

Over coffee, Hawkes offered me a job. He says he is needed in Apalachicola and wants me to continue on his route, picking up the cotton for shipment. As his agent, I would record the bales purchased from each farmer and I would be authorized to issue notes of payment. He said he likes the way I communicate with the farmers. He promises to show me the records he will require. He seems confident I can learn what I need to know before he leaves. I consider him a friend and I am grateful for his trust.

Thomas loved working for Hawkes.

6 Apalachicola

CITY OF APALACHICOLA.

June 23, 1851

Dear Diary,

Working for Hawkes is a dream come true. I meet with farmers, men who remind me of my father and our *neighbors. I work my way up and down the rivers, stopping at the landings to purchase bales of cotton. I have traveled in Georgia as far south as Bainbridge, but it is my trips to Apalachicola I love best. Apalachicola is a thriving port. Vessels beyond my imagination dot her harbor.*

There are four types of vessels common in Apalachicola: ships, barks, brigs, and schooners. All are sailing vessels, but the ships with their square-rigged masts are considered the blue-bloods of the seas. The first time I saw a ship with full sail framed by the morning sun, it took my breath away.

There is a constant motion to the port, ships arriving and departing, loading and unloading. Crowds of people stroll along the docks or crowd the taverns on the waterfront.

When Thomas arrived at the port in 1852, it would be his last trip.

December 14, 1852

Dear Diary,

I had a good feeling when I arrived in Apalachicola. My trip has been successful and I had a large load of cotton to deliver. The day was beautiful and sunny. The sun shimmered on the water as I walked along the docks. Hawkes was meeting with his partners and he told me to wait for him at the corner tavern. I found a little table where I could watch and listen.

I overheard a group of men discussing two new ports just to the east. A hurricane had wiped out the established port, Port Leon, in 1843.

A large Irishman with a reddish beard told his companions about the storm. "The storm was so vicious, nothing was left standing from the old port. I tell you, there was no trace at high tide. At low tide, you could see some of the pylons and debris where the docks had been. The warehouses full of cotton, the houses, and the town store, the Inn—all gone without a sign they had ever been there."

He took a big swig of his ale, gave a large belch, and went on about the agents. "The docks and warehouses were a total loss to the agents in place. Those poor devils had paid for the cotton and were ready to ship when they were wiped out. Many of the agents were bankrupt. Most of the others were just hanging on, except for Daniel Lord. Lord has a horseshoe up his butt, he does. He owns the fastest little vessel in the area and shipped before the storm. Lucky, he is."

He told his friends about two new ports that are vying for the trade, Newport and St. Marks. By the time Hawkes and his partners finished their *meeting and Hawkes made his way to the tavern, I had made a decision.*

This was the opportunity Thomas had been looking for. He signed over the cotton he had delivered and, with a letter of introduction from Hawkes, booked passage aboard the *Spray*.

7 Newport, 1852

The year 1852 was a year of change for both Thomas and me. It was the year Fate began to weave our sorrow and our joy into the life that would bind us. It was the year my mother died. I was only two when I lost her. It was the year Thomas, then twenty-one years old, sailed from Apalachicola to Newport on the one-hundred-eighteen-ton steamer, the *Spray*.

The *Spray* was owned by Daniel Lord, the largest cotton agent in the area. Lord was both a cotton agent and a factor; he supplied a full service to the farmers he dealt with by loaning them money to cover planting costs, collecting and selling the crop, and then taking a percent commission on the sale to repay the money loaned.

The *Spray* carried passengers between Apalachicola and St. Marks or Newport. The St. Marks River was a beautiful, crystal clear river but very shallow at low tide, making it impossible for larger ships to navigate.

Just off the town of St. Marks was a deep waterhole known to the locals as the "Spanish Hole." The larger ships anchored offshore at the Spanish Hole, and then from there, the *Spray*, with its shallow draw, "lightered" cargo to warehouses in St. Marks and Newport.

Daniel Lord collected from the other cotton agents for the service, as well as provided service for his own customers.

Lord was an energetic businessman with business interests in cotton, tobacco, salt, sugar cane, and the shipping of each. The *Spray* also delivered mail along the Florida coast. When it needed repairs, Lord opened a foundry, saying it was easier than waiting for parts to arrive. Now when farmers needed a tool or wagon wheel repaired, they took it to the foundry in Newport.

December 21, 1852

Dear Diary,

On my voyage to Newport, I met Bowlegs, Lord's slave and mate on the Spray. I am accustomed to talking to a ship's crew and asked Bowlegs about the hurricane that destroyed the old port. Bowlegs told me that the hurricane's force pushed the water ashore so fiercely it destroyed everything in its path. It pushed so hard the pilings gave way; a barge broke loose with four slaves and a white man aboard. The barge was swept out to sea, and the men were never seen again.

I was fascinated by the story and asked about the Spray, her draw, and her speed. Bowlegs bragged about the quick, little vessel and wanted to hear about the steamers I had traveled on.

He was especially interested in the Edwin Forest.

I told him the Edwin Forest has six boilers and two engines with twenty horsepower each. He was impressed by her power. We talked for hours. At one point, Bowlegs asked me why I always smiled when I talked about the Eufaula. I only paused for a moment before I answered, "It must be the memory of the beautiful women."

Bowlegs laughed. "Yeah, a beautiful woman can make a man stay when he should go."

Thomas arrived in Wakulla County with the letter from Hawkes introducing him as having worked as a cotton agent. It professed his good character and honest nature. The years on the rivers and Sam Henry's conservative example, had given Thomas funds to purchase land. He planned to farm the land and open a cotton gin of his own.

Thomas took a room at the Newport Inn and went to meet the man he had heard so much about, Daniel Lord.

Thomas and Lord became friends quickly. Thomas could readily talk about the cotton market and he appreciated Lord's endeavors. Over the next few months, the two talked daily.

January 21, 1853

Dear Diary,

I am impressed with Daniel Lord. He has interest in many areas and seems to make all of them profitable. He keeps meticulous records and has a memory for details.

We frequently talk about the 1843 hurricane. He told me he chose to rebuild in Newport because he had seen the aftermath of the hurricane. "The storm raged across the Gulf," he said, "and exploded when it hit the land, demolishing everything in sight."

I look forward to our talks and take care with his advice.

Lord had warehouses in Newport, and the port at St. Marks had a mule-drawn railroad that provided transit to Tallahassee and Quincy. Thomas wanted land somewhere between the ports and not too far from the railroad, the Pin Hook Road to the east, and the Plank Road to the north. He wrote home about the beautiful land, the spreading oaks, and especially the clear water springs that dotted the area. Thomas settled on land north of Crawfordville in Wakulla County. It wasn't long before his brother Milton joined him. Milton and Thomas cleared the land and began work on the cotton gin and house.

In the spring of 1853, Thomas's cotton gin was ready for operation, and he was eager to court a young beauty from church.

April 7, 1854

Dear Diary,

There are a number of attractive young women in the area but none as lovely as Bethany Duncan. She has dark eyes that sparkle when she speaks and she lights up a room with her smile. Milton has taken a job as a clerk for Lord. I hired Bethany's younger brother James to help build my barn.

April 24, 1854

Dear Diary,

I have never told James I have had Bethany in mind as we built, but he has to know I have been asking a lot of questions about his sister. I usually look for the Duncan family after services, talking about the weather or the work James is doing. Today, I was about to ask for permission to court Bethany when an announcement was made. Bethany will marry a seminary student from Tallahassee. I usually stay and visit after church but not this day. I was afraid my disappointment would show.

That would be Thomas's last diary entry of any consequence. The cotton gin and farm needed ledgers and supply lists. I will always be grateful for the letters he sent.

8 Henry James Bradford

Thomas wrote home often. Milton returned his letters for years, then it was Sam who answered. He gave Thomas all the county news. He reported on the weather, how the crops were faring and, of course, the county deaths and births.

Over the years, Thomas could not help but notice there were no baby announcements from Clayton and Louise. Sam and his wife, Mary Alice, had three daughters in five years. The only mention of a new Bradford had come two years before, when Thomas had first arrived in Wakulla County. Sam wrote to say that Clayton and Louise had adopted me.

June 2, 1852

Dear Thomas,

My sister has long awaited a child and it is with great joy that I write to say Clayton and Louise have adopted a boy. Clayton's cousin, James Bradford, lost his wife in childbirth and needed help with his boy, Henry, making it a fitting arrangement for all.

In Friendship Always,

Sam

Clayton and Louise started out as happy as a couple could be. People said they were both beautiful inside and out, an excellent match. Sarah Bradford was sure she had the perfect mother for her grandchildren.

During the first year that Clayton and Louise were married, when another couple announced they were expecting, Sarah would say, "Louise will surely be next." Every year that passed brought children to others while Louise felt a growing despair. Clayton tried to hide his own disappointment; he loved Louise and supported her. The worst was the look in Sarah's eyes. She could not hide her disappointment.

The Bradford family was considered wealthy. They had three slaves: Moses, Mae, and their son Elijah. They worked mostly for Sarah and William but helped Clayton and Louise when needed. Mae would help Louise with the laundry or the garden and was always there for canning. Moses helped Clayton and his father with the plowing, while Elijah tended to the animals. Elijah had a gift for working with the animals. He seemed to understand them, and they responded to his kindness.

Clayton was now a married man and, without his brother, rarely raced, but he still loved fast horses. When he attended an auction near Macon to purchase a bull for his fledgling herd, he came home with a sturdy bull and the most beautiful, sleek horse the county had ever seen.

Raider had been matched in a race against the best available. He was as fast as the wind and could turn on a dime. The horse had easily won the event. After the race, admirers surrounded the strong-willed, almost arrogant, animal. He stepped high and held his head upright, showing off for his audience. Clayton was totally smitten.

When Clayton brought the horse home, neighbors and friends crowded the barn to see the magnificent animal. Raider's coat shone from the brushing and care Elijah gave him. The spirited horse gained a reputation for being difficult to handle, but he followed Elijah's every direction. So much so, Elijah's care caught the attention of a doctor from Colquitt.

The doctor watched Elijah with the horse and later with the family's hunting dogs. That night, the doctor came to the elder Bradford and offered to buy the young boy, but William Bradford rejected the proposal. He knew the way the boy handled the animals made him an asset. The doctor was persistent and raised the offer twice. Finally, Bradford agreed. Louise could see the terrible pain on Mae's face when Elijah was sold.

The week after Elijah was taken to Colquitt, Sarah came by to announce a new Bradford had been born. Clayton's cousin, James, had a son. They named the boy Henry James Bradford. As Sarah left, she commented, "At least someone is carrying on the Bradford name." Louise was stung by the remark.

Mae came into the kitchen after working in the garden, and she found Louise in a puddle of tears. The two women spent the day shelling and cooking the peas Mae had picked. When I was older, Louise would tell me, "We seasoned them with tears and prayers."

I was the baby Sarah had talked about. My mother died two years later while delivering my sister, Mary, who lived only a few days. My father had no way to care for a toddler. He brought me to Clayton's farm and asked if he and Louise would take me. Louise, desperate for a child, took me into her arms and became my angel.

9   Leaving Dooly County

I barely remember my father. Fishing at the lake is my best memory of Uncle Clayton. We had only been a family for a few years when word came my father married a widow from just across the river in Alabama. She had three boys and Louise was sure they would come back for me. Life sure can turn on you. While Louise was all in a tizzy about keeping me with her, she lost Clayton.

Without Clayton, living in Dooly County was unbearable for Louise. Sarah took to her bed with uncontrollable grief. William sat on the porch and stared for hours at a time.

Sam Marsh wrote to Thomas telling him the sad news about their old friend.

November 3, 1854

Dear Thomas,

Your parents are both well and send their love. It is with a heavy heart that I write to you. I know you were close to both Jackson and Clayton Bradford, and I have always known you held Louise in high regard. On the 23rd of October, Clayton lost his life. He was plowing a new field when he hit a jacket nest. His mule backed into the plow entangling it. Clayton must have tried to free the animal and was killed by his kick. The only blessing is he died quickly.

Clayton and Louise were married almost nine years but have no children of their own. As I wrote, they adopted Clayton's cousin's son, Henry, two years ago. Mary Alice and I have tried to console her, but Louise is beside herself with loss. I hope this letter finds you and Milton in good health and that you can find the time to send some words of comfort to Louise. I am concerned about her and fear for her health.

In Friendship Always,

Sam

When Sam's letter arrived, Thomas wrote back immediately.

December 21, 1854

Dear Sam,

I am deeply saddened to hear the news about our friend. It is hard to imagine both brothers taken. Please give Louise my sincere sympathy and the note I have enclosed. Milton and I know what a fine man Clayton was and grieve his passing.

A terrible loss like this makes loved ones even dearer. It has been too long since I have been home and I hope to visit soon. I look forward to seeing my family, friends, and neighbors.

Please give my love to Mary Alice and the girls, and let my mother know all is well with Milton,

Thomas

Thomas continued to write to Louise. It wasn't long before one of the letters included a proposal.

The cotton crop is harvested in late October, November, or early December in North Florida. The following year, Thomas worked the cotton gin as hard as he could. He arrived in Dooly County the week before Christmas in 1855.

Louise used the traditional waiting time for a widow to sell Raider and the livestock. Raider turned out to be a good investment. He had sired a few colts of exceptional quality and brought top dollar. When Clayton died, half the county would have bet it was the feisty Raider that had been his demise.

Louise organized our belongings and we were ready when Thomas arrived.

Thomas and Louise were married in a small ceremony attended only by family. It was held at the little church where he had first fallen in love with her. Milton had stayed in Florida to care for the farm, but Thomas had Sam at his side.

I'm embarrassed to say what I remember most about their wedding was Grandma Marsh letting me have two pieces of cake. It had a rich buttercream icing that melted in my mouth. Louise wore her best Sunday dress and carried a bouquet of narcissus I helped to pick. At the altar, I stood next to Sam and Thomas. It was the first time I met Thomas. He had eyes as grey as a winter sky, but they danced with light when Louise walked toward us.

I stayed the night with Grandma Marsh. In the morning, Thomas and Louise arrived in a mule-drawn wagon loaded with what was left of our lives in Dooly County. Thomas gave me my Christmas present, a bulldog puppy. It was a cold morning. I hugged my new puppy and wrapped one of our quilts around both of us. He licked my face and I never felt warmer. We named him "Dooly" as we left for our new life in Florida.

10 A Florida New Year

We camped our way to Crawfordville. The wagon had a full load, making progress slow. It seemed that Louise and Thomas could talk all day long. They started to tell the stories I would love. The stories I would one day tell.

At night, we sat under the stars. Thomas would point out the constellations he knew. Orion was my favorite. His belt had three stars aligned and Sirius, the bright "dog" star, followed him faithfully across the winter sky. I pictured Dooly following me and it gave me a thrill. Louise seemed happier with each day.

We finally stopped near a small clearing surrounded by woods. A wooden building was at the center of the clearing, the cotton gin. A mule would circle it, turning the gears that powered the operation. It wasn't much to look at. Thomas assured Louise it worked well and would eventually make a profit. We turned at the gin, and there at the end of the little lane was our new home.

It wasn't as big as the one we left, but we loved it right from the start. The two small buildings were made from rough-cut lumber and connected by a covered porch. Each building had a limerock fireplace, one on the right, and one on the left, binding the two with a kind of symmetry. The first room was the kitchen. Kitchens were separated from the living and sleeping areas because of the intense heat and fear of fire. The second room had porches on all sides. It was both a sitting room and a bedroom. A narrow staircase led to a loft, which would be my room.

A small fence protected the house and garden. The yard in front of the house was shaded by huge live oak trees that dripped with moss. We had a barn, a hen house, and a corn crib. The best part was a small spring that provided clear, sweet water.

We would start our new life and a new year, 1856, in Florida. On New Year's Day, we met our neighbors. Milton had traveled the back roads, inviting friends and neighbors to meet his new sister-in-law. Wagons began to arrive before lunch. The guests covered tables with wild turkey, ham, cornbread, pots of greens, and squash. One table had nothing but seafood. I had never eaten shrimp, crab, oysters, or mullet fresh from the Gulf of

Mexico. The seafood gave off the most enticing smells I could imagine.

Jake, a large man with a long, dark beard, played a fiddle. Everyone smiled, laughed, and danced throughout the day. They all made a fuss over Louise, saying they saw why Thomas had traveled so far. Most told Thomas what a fine son I was, and it was agreed that Dooly was sure to be a great "hog dog."

Florida history has been kept alive by telling the stories one man to the next, one generation to the next. One of the oldtimers recalled a story he had been told. "Christopher Columbus brought eight hogs to the West Indies. The hogs reproduced rapidly. Hernando De Soto brought thirteen of their descendants from Cuba to Florida to feed his men." The man explained how the hogs now filled the tables of rural Florida. "The hogs have their ears notched to mark their ownership. They roam the swamps most of the year, finding their own food. Dogs like Dooly help to catch the hogs for their owners."

I was getting sleepy when Milton stood and proposed a toast. "Thomas and I have made our home here and we can't be thankful enough for the good friends and neighbors we have found. This lovely lady was my neighbor and friend like most of you here tonight. My brother wasn't blessed with my amicable nature and handsome face, so the day Louise agreed to marry him was the luckiest day of his life." He paused for the laughter to quiet. "Louise is not only beautiful but as kind and good as they come. I hope you will all join me in welcoming Louise, Henry, and Dooly, and congratulate Thomas on his good fortune." The group erupted with cheers and shouts of goodwill.

Louise was invited to join the other ladies in a Bible study group. Dooly and I were invited to go hunting as soon as we were both a little older.

The music lasted late into the night. The sky was clear and the stars so bright I felt I could reach out and touch them. I can still close my eyes and feel the warmth of the fires on that cold winter night. I can see the happy faces, hear the music, smell and taste my first seafood treats. Florida was home.

11 Bowlegs and Neea

I first met Bowlegs the day after the welcome party. About mid-morning, he drove one of the foundry wagons up the narrow drive to our house. Bowlegs arrived with the most beautiful woman my eyes had ever seen.

Neea was a Seminole Indian with the blood of undefeated warriors and the courage of runaway slaves in her veins. She had skin the color of copper and her eyes were a golden amber. Neea had long, wavy, black hair that shone like a raven's wing. She looked straight ahead and never at me, but I couldn't take my eyes off her.

Bowlegs walked to the house and gave Thomas a sack of greens from their garden as a wedding gift. Thomas and Louise thanked him and praised the quality of the produce.

As Thomas and I walked him back to the wagon, I imitated the various comments from the night before. I stuck my hand out and said, "Bowlegs, you sure are lucky to have a real beauty for a wife." No one said a word. Finally, Bowlegs took my hand with a huge grin. He told Thomas, "This young man has a real eye for the ladies." The two men locked their eyes as if sharing a private joke.

The copper lady never moved a muscle, but as Bowlegs turned the wagon around, her eyes smiled at me.

Later, I asked Thomas why they called him Bowlegs. His legs didn't look bowed to me. Thomas explained it is a term for a sailor. "When he first sailed on the *Spray,* his friends on the dock told him to be careful he didn't get 'them bowlegs' and the name stuck."

Thomas said it was his name that helped him win the lovely Neea. "Another Bowlegs—Billy Bowlegs— was a famous Seminole chief." Bowlegs had been among a group of slaves cutting timber when a small band of Seminoles came by to trade with them. The slaves had a wagon from the foundry that held extra tools—hatchets, axes, and wedges for splitting the wood, as well as a few hoes and a saw. The Seminoles wanted to trade a deer for some of the tools in the wagon. The Seminole men were told they had to talk to Bowlegs and they quickly took to the dark bear of a man. The women were hiding in a nearby stand of trees. The men trusted Bowlegs enough to call the women out of the hammock to meet the man named after the great chief.

Bowlegs fell in love at first sight. He went back to the foundry and gathered every usable piece of discarded metal he could find. He spent the next month making the tools he knew they wanted and more. When the tools were complete, he met with the Seminoles and traded the tools for Neea.

12 Mysterious Waters

It didn't take us long to get into a regular routine in our new home. Louise made us breakfast before daylight. She worked in her garden, tending the squash, cucumbers, tomatoes, peas, and beans while Thomas cleared the fields for corn. Our fields had an unlimited supply of stumps and limerock that had to be cleared before we could plow. I helped Louise with the cooking, sweeping, even the laundry. I helped Thomas with the animals, and I took care of Dooly. The first thing I had to teach him was not to chase the chickens. Then I taught him to sit and stay. We played fetch until he was so tired he would just flop down in the cool dirt.

Our house was between the St. Marks River and the Sopchoppy River, just north of the county seat, Crawfordville. The word Wakulla is a Timucuan Indian word that means "mysterious waters." Wakulla County is teeming with waterways.

We had been there a few months and the weather had warmed when Thomas announced he wanted to go fishing, and he wanted us to go with him. We hitched the mule to the wagon. Louise packed a basket, and we traveled ten miles to the beach. I had never seen such a wonder. The water stretched on well out of sight, waves rolled ashore, and the smell of salt filled the air. Thomas and I fished for dinner. Louise took off her stockings and held up her skirt to wade in the surf while Dooly barked at the waves and chased the seabirds. We cooked our fish right there on the beach and didn't leave until we had just enough light to get home. Dooly and I fell asleep in the wagon, both of us worn out by the travel, the sun, and the salt.

Every few weeks after that, Thomas made an announcement. "The fish are biting, I feel it in my bones." We would leave the chores behind and set out on an adventure. Sometimes he took us back to the beach and sometimes he took us to one of the rivers. Rivers crisscross Wakulla County. The St. Marks and Wakulla rivers are crystal clear, the Sopchoppy and Ochlockonee darker, and the Aucilla so black it mirrors the trees, making it look like they're both above and below us all at once.

At the headwaters of the Wakulla River, a spring gushes water from deep in the aquifer. The water is clear, sweet, and cool year round. Over the springs, the water is deeper than any of the men could say. Thomas helped me swim out to the deepest part where I could see the bones of some prehistoric beast resting on a rocky shelf.

The edges are shallow, and the bottom is sandy, making it an inviting place to swim. Most any afternoon, people were at the springs or just down the river. On Saturdays, we usually saw our neighbors at one or the other of the swimming holes. When it was really hot, a group of women would remove their dresses and swim in their undergarments just like the rest of us. The women stayed together, forming a circle to keep their modesty. The center of the circle was filled with the youngest children, squealing with delight.

I can testify that Florida in the 1800s had more than its share of biting insects of every kind. There were gnats so tiny they were called "no see ums." You didn't know they were there until they bit you. We had biting flies of every description, some big enough to hit with a stick. The mosquitoes, ticks, and chiggers were ferocious enough to drive a man insane. The land is low and easily flooded. Storms coming off the Gulf were a constant concern. We had black bears, monster alligators, water moccasins, rattlesnakes, wild cats, and intense heat that lasted most of the year. But we were a family there. And we were happy.

13 Chief

The day before my tenth birthday, Thomas and a much older man came up our road with a pony in tow, my birthday present. Thomas announced, "It's time for you to have your own way to go. After all, you are nearly grown and ready for the responsibility."

Dooly ran in circles barking at the pony's feet. The pony kept his head high, unbothered by Dooly. It was like he knew that one well-placed kick would make a dog show some respect. I was as excited as Dooly and wanted to know all about my new pony.

Thomas and I were both fascinated by the history of our adopted state. We listened intently while the old man talked about my pony. "Ponce de Leon brought horses to Florida for his officers and scouts in the 1500s. Later, Spanish expeditions like De Soto added to the Florida horse population. Some call them Seminole ponies and some call them Chickasaw. It was really the hogs that started the Chickasaw herd."

I stroked the pony's mane as the man went on. "De Soto carried descendants of the hogs he brought from Cuba as he traveled west. He shared some of the pork with the Chickasaw. The Chickasaw loved the meat. Three Chickasaw men helped themselves to some of De Soto's pigs. De Soto killed two of the pig thieves and cut the hands off of the third man. De Soto also demanded that the Chickasaw give De Soto two hundred Chickasaw women to make up for the theft. The Chickasaws, like the Seminoles, were a no-nonsense tribe. They responded to De Soto's demands with a late night attack. They brought live coals in clay pots and set fire to his camp. When the smoke cleared, the Spanish had lost twelve men, fifty-seven horses, and four hundred of their precious pigs.

"The herds of Spanish ponies owned by the Seminoles and those of the Chickasaw shared a heritage and, through trade and shared destiny, blended. They are the horse breed used by Florida cattlemen because of their agility and speed."

My pony was a bay. His coat was reddish brown, and his mane, tail, and socks were black. I named him "Chief" in honor of his heritage.

14 A Season for War

Most of what I know about the August family, I learned secondhand. The wealthier the family, the more there was to talk about at gatherings. The August family was the largest landowner in Gadsden County and the first to hold a political rally, the first to talk about war.

Slaveowners, the family raised cotton, corn, and tobacco. Aaron August was the oldest son, and everyone said he was an intelligent young man with high potential. His father sent him to school in Atlanta, hoping he would study law. Aaron found getting by on his charm more appealing than the study required for a law degree.

He met Arielle Winters at a Christmas party his fraternity brother had asked him to attend. Her family was one of the most successful shipping families in Savannah. Arielle was visiting her Atlanta relatives for the holiday. While she wasn't the prettiest girl in the room, she was definitely attractive, tall with dark eyes and a warm smile. Her wealthy upbringing gave her confidence and poise. The minute they were introduced, Aaron was sure he would make her his wife. He considered his land and her family money to be a perfect match.

Arielle was scheduled to return to Savannah after the New Year, but Aaron encouraged her to extend her visit. He used the time to win her heart and he proposed on Valentine's Day. The two went immediately to Savannah to meet her parents and secure their approval. Arielle began planning a wedding while Aaron met with the architect to construct a columned mansion like the homes he coveted. Aaron August and Arielle Winters would name their new home, "All Seasons Plantation."

All Seasons Plantation was build and maintained with slave labor. True to its name, the entire house and gardens were redecorated for each season. The centerpieces, the seat cushions, and even the china would change to match the calendar. The themes reflected the wild game, birds, and flowers known to prosper in each season. The home became the showcase of Gadsden County.

When All Seasons Plantation held its first rally, William Hart, the sheriff of Gadsden County, went about shaking hands and inviting the men he considered "influential" to the rally and cook-out. Thomas had ginned cotton for the plantation once and was eager to attract more of their business, like most of those invited, he jumped at the chance.

The rally was in late October 1859. The plantation was spectacular. Mums filled the yards, and porches displayed every shade of red and gold. Apples and gourds were mixed into the centerpieces, sturdy bucks were displayed on tapestries, and wild turkeys adorned the china in the formal dining room.

Arielle was an excellent hostess. She walked among her guests, making a connection with each. At some point, one of the men told Arielle, "I sure do like how you celebrate the seasons."

She responded, "The poets believe our lives have seasons, as well."

Thomas was standing near and recited the first two lines of Keats's "The Human Season," one of Catherine Brooks's favorites:

Four Seasons fill the measure of the year;
There are four seasons in the mind of man

Arielle was intrigued. She asked, "What does Keats say about autumn?"

The story was, Thomas gave Arielle a slight bow as he quoted:

His soul has it Autumn, when his wings

77

He furleth close, content so to look
On mists in idleness—to let fair things
Pass by unheeded as a threshold brook.

Arielle took Thomas by the arm and walked him around her gardens. A huge outdoor barbeque was arranged for the many men who had traveled for the rally. The smell of meat cooking on a spit filled the night air. Long, wooden tables were scattered around the yard, each covered with bowls of beans and cornbread. The family members, other plantation owners from the area, and the most prestigious guests were invited to the formal dining room.

Arielle had a place at her table set for Thomas. He ate across from Arielle's cousin, Charlotte, and just down from Daniel Lord. Thomas couldn't help but think it was his mother's determination that her young sons get an education that earned him a seat in the elegant dining room. Thanks to Jackson's friendship, he hadn't missed a line.

Arielle's family was active in both shipping and politics, and a number of her relatives attended the rally. Her cousin, Ezra Winters, a born politician, was the principal speaker. He knew how to captivate the crowd and, with a liberal amount of liquor, how to motivate action just short of frenzy.

Most of the talk was about self-determination and state's rights. Everyone was in agreement: the industrial states shouldn't impose tariffs on the southern states or tell us what we should do or not do. If something as powerful as a state could lose their rights, what chance did an individual man have?

The rally lasted late into the night. Thomas and the other Wakulla County participants camped on the way home. It was late morning before they returned. Thomas went directly to his favorite chair under the live oak in the front yard, propped his feet up, and slept until dinner.

Louise didn't say anything, but she banged around the kitchen enough to show her displeasure. Thomas talked at dinner about the grand plantation. He went on and on about the hospitality, the food, and the intelligence of the speakers.

It was weeks later that Louise and I learned Thomas had been invited to the formal dinner and how Arielle August had paraded him around on her arm. I had never seen Louise jealous before, but she was then.

At the end of January, another rally was held near Tallahassee at Crossroads Plantation, and again, Thomas was invited. The August family would attend, and Ezra Winters would again be one of the speakers.

It was the first time I ever heard Thomas and Louise argue. She was dead set against Thomas going. The more she pushed, the more he pushed back. At one point, she told him, "Arielle August doesn't bend her back or fight the heat, mosquitoes, and flies while working in the garden. I have more in common with Arielle August's slaves than I have with Arielle August, and so do you."

Slavery was the unspoken issue. Thomas was torn. He couldn't help but think of the beating he had witnessed. He tried to explain, "A man has a duty."

Louise continued to protest.

Finally, Thomas embraced her, stopping the argument by saying, "And a man has a responsibility to protect what he loves."

He went to the rally, but when he returned, the house was awful quiet. Thomas seemed weighed down by the decisions ahead.

After that, rallies were commonplace, and secession was the central topic of discussion. Politics even spilled over to church yards after services. Thomas was invited to the Democratic State Convention. When he returned, he and Louise avoided talking about the possibility of war, but I could tell they were both worried. They didn't talk to me about it, but Thomas started waking in the middle of the night just to sit on the porch and Louise's eyes were often red at breakfast.

15 Milton

Daniel Lord was a man who liked to know where every penny went. He kept records of all of his transactions. He hired Milton to keep the accounts for the foundry, but soon had him moving from one of his enterprises to the other, keeping the accounts for each.

Milton was needed in Newport for most of his duties, and he took a room at the Newport Inn. Louise wasn't pleased about Milton staying at the inn. The women at church gossiped that it had a reputation for providing young slave girls for more than room service. Many in the south opposed slavery, but to say anything against it was financial suicide. The wealthy slave owners held the purse strings in most communities.

Milton was sitting on the porch of the hotel when he first saw Carrie Andrews. Carrie had silky blonde hair and a fresh beauty that attracted Milton. Her joyful nature made the two an immediate match. Carrie's family was from Coweta County, Georgia.

Her father was a farmer near Newman. Carrie's uncle, William Andrews, was a carpenter in Newport. He built strong, well-crafted furniture. His son, Charles, and daughter-in-law, Grace, were both teachers.

Carrie's father was more than displeased with Allen Jones, the rascal who had been trying to court her. The boy had a quick temper, and when he drank—which was most of the time—he was also quick with his fists. The brothers agreed it would be best for Carrie to come to Newport where she could be an apprentice for Grace and Charles.

I was in Grace Andrews's class. I can read and I'm pretty good with numbers. I would say I was deep center in the class, not the best but not the worst. I was really surprised when Milton started to come by to check on my progress. I understood when I saw how he looked at Carrie.

Before long, Milton was asked to dinner at the Andrews' and they were all invited to join us. I loved having Carrie around. She made Milton happier than I had ever seen him. Thomas and Louise treated her as family from the start.

Milton leased a house near Newport and proposed to Carrie. In October 1860, the two were married. Thomas was the best man, and I was next to him.

That day always stood out in my memory. We were so happy. We didn't know it would be the last of our happy times.

October is always a wonderful month in north Florida and the year of the wedding was especially nice. The wildflowers surrounded us with color. There were long purple spikes of deer tongue and blazing stars mixed with the soft pink of false foxglove. The roads were lined with the tiny yellow tickseed, the larger black-eyed Susan, and stalks of goldenrod. Patches of tiny, white flowers blended among them—dog fennel, frost aster, hat pins, and sedge.

Florida's Gulf Coast is part of the annual butterfly migration route. Hundreds of butterflies attended the wedding, adding color and a delicate grace. Most were monarchs or viceroys with their bright orange and black wings, but they were joined by a host of others adding yellows, blues, and browns to the mix.

That night, we had a party like the one that had welcomed us to Florida. Friends and neighbors came to celebrate. Tables were filled with food. The Presley family, known for their ability to smoke a mullet, brought a mountain of mullet and fresh oysters. Kettles full of boiled shrimp and crabs, hams, and wild turkey invited hungry guests. We had cornbread, squash, butter beans, baked pears, and pecan pies. Jake, the big man with the beard, again played the fiddle. He was joined by another neighbor with a harmonica, filling the celebration with music.

The clear sky made the stars sparkle like diamonds. The moon rose late, giving us a show as it made its way across the sky, outlining the live oaks. A thick, grey moss hung from their branches. A light breeze kept the insects away and swayed the moss in a kind of ghostly dance.

Thomas spoke that night. "I want to say how grateful we are to welcome this beautiful lady to our family. It is easy to see why Milton has given his heart to Carrie and her to him. Carrie is smart and lovely in every way, I have no doubt she will make an excellent wife. Behind Milton's big smile there is a man of substance. My brother's agreeable nature will suit him well as a husband, but his greatest gift is an inner strength I see in few others. Please join me in celebrating this union and wishing them all the blessings of marriage."

I searched the night sky and I made a wish. I wished we could always be as happy as we were that day, but I didn't get my wish. Maybe I jinxed us, wanting it so badly, or maybe so many forces were already in motion that even the brightest stars couldn't change our destiny.

16 The Smallest Tadpole

The talk of war continued. The rallies soon became enlistment opportunities. Florida had only been a state since 1845, but on January 11, 1861, Princess Murat pulled a silk cord that fired a cannon on the Capitol lawn to mark Florida's secession from the Union. I didn't think Tallahassee had a princess, but I guess they did. One of the Northern newspapers called Florida, "the smallest tadpole in the dirty pool of secession."

When war was finally declared, men wanted to know where others stood; a number of them stopped by to speak to Thomas. Thomas was still wrestling with the decision. Like many of our neighbors, he was divided by a sense of duty and conscience. The day Daniel Lord came to our house, I could tell Louise was scared. Lord had a man with him I had never seen.

Lord, born in Maine, came to Florida as a young man and managed to be a successful commission merchant. He had a reputation as an honest man, a man with foresight. When Thomas arrived in Newport, it was Lord he went to with his letter of introduction. Thomas was in awe of his success.

Lord introduced the man with him. "Thomas, I want you to meet Daniel L. Frierson, a good man, a good friend, and the newly appointed Captain for the Wakulla Guards."

Frierson shook Thomas's hand, "I need a Lieutenant I can trust. I asked Lord for a recommendation, and based on that, I'm asking you to accept the appointment."

Even though it was a huge compliment, Thomas hesitated. Then Frierson began to speak about his recruits. He handed Thomas the list. "These are the men who have already signed to be Wakulla Guards."

They were our friends and neighbors. The men talked and Thomas finally accepted. He shook their hands, and they rode off. As he started to the house, Thomas knew telling Louise would be his first battle.

When Thomas reached the house, I was loading the firewood I had gathered into the stove. Louise was silent. Finally, Thomas told her, "You don't know what it's like to be a man. A man has a duty."

"What about your family?" Louise asked.

"I'm trying to protect this family. I don't want another word said about it. I am not a little kid you can boss."

The statement cut Louise to the core. The house stayed awful quiet until May and the official enlistment in Newport.

The Wakulla Guards and their families met in Newport on May 17, 1861. The Guards would become part of the 3rd Florida Infantry. Lord was there, along with the August family. Arielle August looked lovely in her dove gray taffeta gown. Two captains from Jefferson County, Captain Bird and Captain Girardeau, attended the ceremony, as well. Their bearing, crisp new uniforms, and shiny swords helped to make them look very important.

The town was crowded with family members and well-wishers. The Columbia and Suwannee County guard, called the Dixie Stars, brought a drum and fife corps that played throughout the day. The guard from Duval County, the Duval Cowboys, had a group of trick riders that entertained and amazed us. One man could turn completely around in the saddle while the horse ran at full speed. Another could grab a hat off the ground and never slip.

The August family sponsored lunch baskets for the enlistees and their families. Each basket held fried chicken and biscuits. We had just picked up our basket when Martha Duncan came to say hello.

She told Louise, "We are so proud that James is going to be a sergeant. I was worried about him going off until I heard Thomas would be his lieutenant. James has faith in Thomas. I felt like my prayers were answered when Thomas agreed to the lieutenant appointment."

Louise asked Martha to join us and brought out a quilt for us all to sit on. Martha commented as she placed the children on the quilt, "Can you believe the August family is rich enough to provide baskets of chicken to all these families?" She spoke about the money the men were going to be paid, "They're going to give James one hundred and twenty dollars for the use of his horse and twelve dollars for his gun and saddle. I tell you, it is a real blessing. We never dreamed of having that much money at one time."

Martha and James Duncan had been married just a few months before Thomas and Louise. I met James at our welcome party on New Year's, I listened to the adults, I learned he had a beautiful sister and that he helped build our barn and the fence around our house.

James and Martha were very young when they married. James's mother had passed years earlier, so when his sister Bethany married and left home, James joked that he had married because "he couldn't face his father's cooking." Martha was a good cook.

The couple's only daughter had dark hair and eyes and would be as beautiful as her aunt Bethany. As we ate our picnic lunches, the younger of two boys hung to Martha's skirts. The older one, no more than five, kept trying to wander from her view. I think Louise looked at the burden Martha would face without a husband around and she felt ashamed of her own fears.

Aaron August wore a grey, tailored waistcoat and slacks. He was nearly forty and considered too old to serve, but he walked around with a cane, telling everyone how he wished he was going. He mostly stood with the officers, smiling and shaking hands.

Arielle, always the gracious hostess, came around to say hello to everyone. Thomas and James were sitting with us when she stopped to speak to Louise. "I hear you are a Georgia girl. We Georgia girls need to stick together." She invited Louise and me to visit if we ever came to Gadsden County, even though it was unlikely we ever would. She made a comment about how handsome Thomas looked in his lieutenant's uniform. She put a hand on his sleeve. "You hurry home now. We need men that appreciate the poets now more than ever."

We all thanked her for our lunches, and she made her way among the crowd, her silk petticoats swishing. Louise wore a Sunday dress, cotton with a beige background and a dark red stripe. The stripe had faded in the way cotton tends to do. Thomas made a point not to look at Louise as she smoothed her dress.

In our small community, most of the neighbors had been to our house for events, and we had been to theirs. Because we knew each other so well, it was easy to spot the lies. Jessy Larson, a farmer and a good man, was listed on the enlistment papers as thirty-eight years old, but Thomas, Louise, and I had been to a hog roast to honor his fortieth birthday at least a year earlier. Jessy's son William was listed as eighteen, but he had gone to school with me. I turned eleven the week of the enlistment, so I knew William was no more than thirteen. Jessy told us, "I was so upset when William signed up that I decided to sign up, as well. I couldn't let the boy go alone. At first, they told me I was too old, so I followed my son's lead and lied about my age."

A few of the boys listed were not much older than I was. Thomas and I fished with the Presley family. They had two names on the list. Joseph was fourteen and William fifteen. I was tall for my age and already taller than Joseph.

I spotted Bowlegs in the crowd. He smiled at me and I smiled back then lowered my head and scanned around, looking for Neea. When my eyes crossed his path again, he had a huge grin. I had been caught. My face turned red, and I quickly hid from his sight. Bowlegs and the Seminole woman had a place in the swamp nearby. They had a number of children, but each had been given to her family to raise, just in case. Bowlegs didn't want his children to have a master.

The census showed Newport had a population of four hundred forty-one in 1860. Most were poor farmers. They came to Florida as pioneers, clearing the land, fighting the weather, insects and wildlife to feed their families. They came from Georgia or the Carolinas, arriving with a dream of owning their own land, a strong back, and little else.

Only a handful of men owned slaves. Since everybody knew everybody, the slaves could move about to perform their duties. Slaves drove wagons as far as Tallahassee. There wasn't really anywhere for a slave to run. The Gulf of Mexico was to the west and the Atlantic Ocean to the east. They could travel one thousand miles to the north or head south to the swamps with the Seminoles; no direction held much hope. I had heard men say that Bowlegs traveled on the *Spray* as far as Key West, but he always came back. If being a slave was so terrible, why did he come back? I always thought it must be Neea, but I never asked.

Thomas and Louise were loading the wagon when one of the trick riders passed by. I tried to turn in the saddle like he had done. He stopped and asked my name, then he asked, "That your horse, Henry?"

"Yes, sir. Name's Chief," I replied.

"You got you a fine Cracker horse," he said. "You get ready to sell him, you be sure to let me know."

Florida cattlemen used the fast, agile horses and a whip to drive the wild cows out of the swamps. The whip made a cracking sound, giving the cowboys their name. He tipped his hat as he rode off, and I had a grin a mile wide.

The wagon was loaded and we were ready to head home when a parade of women came by to ask Thomas, as the lieutenant, to protect their men. Thomas and Louise were both quiet on the way home. Louise and the other women who would have no man to help with the farm were already worried. Thomas's mouth was set tight. I think the responsibility ahead of him was setting in too.

Captain Frierson had orders to meet with the rest of the guards on August 10, 1861, in Midway near All Seasons Plantation. That gave everyone a little time to supply their families and gather feed for their livestock. At least one of the families was expecting a baby and Thomas made a comment to Louise I wasn't supposed to hear. "The delay is going to result in additional pregnancies for sure," he said.

I spoke to Thomas about going with him. We both knew I was too young and Louise would never have it. He said I was needed here. "I need you to help Louise, to look out for the families of the men that will go with me, and I need you to keep Dooly away from Mr. Schuler's hound dogs." Mr. Schuler loved his hounds. He wanted his puppies to be hounds, not bulldogs, and he had threatened to shoot Dooly more than once. "You have a big job ahead," Thomas added. At the time, I didn't realize what a big job it was going to be.

17 The Western Army of the Confederacy

Most of what I know about the war, I learned first from letters that Thomas wrote to us and from veterans willing to tell their stories. Later, details found their way to North Florida.

I woke early on the morning of August 10, 1861. Chief and I followed Thomas to the St. Marks Railroad. I watched as the Wakulla Guards headed north, following the tracks to Tallahassee. They left well before daylight without a big to-do. It was best that way. They didn't want to leave in a sea of tears.

Thomas wrote to Louise and me when he could.

August 12, 1861

Dearest Louise,

In Tallahassee, we were joined by two Jefferson County units, the Beauregards and the Rifles. Our group arrived in Midway late in the afternoon. The Duval Cowboys, St. Augustine Blues, Hernando Guards, and the Dixie Stars, the group from Columbia and Suwannee counties, were already in camp. The Madison Grey Eagles were the last to arrive.

The Dixie Stars included a number of musicians. They had time to set up and play, helping the Grey Eagles to make a grand entrance. Their Captain, Thomas Langford, rides a large palomino as gold and shiny as his brass buttons. The silver of his sword blended with the grey of his uniform, shining silver and gold. Our spirits soared.

I miss you and Henry every day and send all of my love,

Thomas

Our days were long without Thomas. We had our chores and his as well.

August 30, 1861

Dearest Louise,

The last three weeks have been an exciting time. The county guards have been formed into companies within the 3rd Florida Infantry. The Wakulla Guard is assigned to Company D. Our days are filled with maneuvers designed to organize an army for travel. At night, there is laughter and contests of every kind. Of course, marksmanship contests and horse races count the most. The Duval Cowboys are the best riders. They win most of the races; if they lose, it is the horse that beats them, not the rider.

There are dice games, horseshoe contests, poker games, penny pitching, arm wrestling, even spitting contests. Around the fires, you can hear tall tales of every kind. Jake Lewis is the best marksmen in the Wakulla group. Will Presley said, "He was either too poor or too cheap to waste a shot." Will is a cutup that keeps the group laughing. His handsome looks and quick humor remind me of Jackson. The Dixie Stars serenade the camp late into the night. Every day brings something exciting.

I miss you both and pray each day our time apart will be short.

All my love to you and Henry,

Thomas

Rumors spread that they would fight against shoe salesmen and factory workers, men who had never even mounted a horse. The factories in the north were dirty and the hours long. Workers there were barely able to feed themselves. I've heard it called "wage slavery."

During the first week in September 1861, the 3rd Florida Infantry set out to meet the Western Army of the Confederacy in northern Mississippi.

September 27, 1861

Dearest Louise,

The night before we traveled, the ladies of Jefferson County presented the regiment with a beautiful silk banner. The banner read, "We Yield but in death." We cheered and even fired shots into the air to celebrate the banner, but it was a reminder of the dangerous situation ahead. Many of us had trouble sleeping that night.

We broke camp and headed to the Chattahoochee River. Our orders are to go by steamer to Columbus. As we approached the river, I saw the steamer, River Bride, come into sight. I learned the River Bride was built in Columbus in 1859. Her sleek lines, new paint, and shiny rails immediately impressed me. I announced to the company, "Boys, you are about to have one of the grandest rides on the river." They cheered for two minutes solid and threw fifty hats in the air.

Columbus is one of the largest manufacturing cities in the south. The size was a little overwhelming to some of the men. I could feel their anxiety rising as we neared the city.

The Florida Infantry was well received. Crowds turned out to welcome us. Bands played, flags were waved. Even a few kisses were had. The heroes' reception boosted our morale.

From Columbus, we traveled by rail to Montgomery, Alabama. At Montgomery, we received a change of orders and are being sent to Mobile to guard the city.

All my love to you and Henry,

Thomas

The 3rd Florida Infantry remained in Mobile for months. Louise and I had Christmas with Milton and Carrie, but it wasn't the same without Thomas.

February 21, 1862

Dearest Louise,

We all miss our loved ones and have concern for our farms. The time away has been hard on all. Some of the boys are so young, they've never spent the night away from family before their enlistment. I worry daily about the burden you and Henry face.

We received orders to travel north. Mobile has offered some comfort to us. The Gulf Coast and saltmarshes are familiar surroundings. The town has supplies, and the churches have provided home-cooked meals when they can. We will depart soon, and pray our letters will not be too delayed by the travel.

All of my love to you and Henry,

Thomas

The 1st and 3rd Florida Infantry headed north toward Chattanooga.

March 10, 1862

Dearest Louise,

We departed Mobile and, within hours, the rains began. A tropical storm came off the Gulf and heavy rains have punished us for days. The roads are mush, and our supply wagons are constantly bogged down. There is no music at night or fire to give the men comfort. One night, lightning was so close, some said their hair stood on end. Hunting is poor; all of the animals are hunkered down. Cooking has become an issue, and food has been rationed. Morale was already low from the storms when we lost our first man.

The constant motion and short rations has caused most to drop weight. Jeffrey Taylor said his uniform was so big and wet it "chafed his ass." Taylor

developed boils from the chafing and
the poor hygiene travel affords. It was
difficult for him to walk or even sit. He
was placed in the supply wagon, but he
didn't seem to improve. His fever and
chills were aggravated by the exposure.

I was asked to ride ahead and join
Captain Frierson the day the
ambulance wagon arrived. The driver
had orders to pick up Taylor. Corporal
Morgan received the orders, and he
was told, "Taylor is to be cared for and
assigned to the ambulance corp."

Taylor begged Morgan, "You can't
leave me behind. I just need to rest
some."

Morgan was torn by the decision. He
said he couldn't imagine being
separated from his Florida neighbors.
He went to our Sergeant, James
Duncan, for help. By now Taylor's fever
soared, and the ambulance driver
shoved the orders forward, forcing a

decision. The camp has been awfully quiet since.

I send all my love to you and Henry,

Thomas

There was never any word from Taylor after that day.

18 The Home Front

What I remember most about the first few months after Thomas left was how lost Louise and I felt. We worked in the garden and cared for the animals. Even Dooly moped around. Milton and Carrie's visits were the only times we smiled or laughed. Milton helped with the farm and he took me fishing whenever he could.

If we had a good catch, we took some to the families we knew needed help. When I took fish to Martha Duncan, I cleaned them for her and spent time playing with her boys, Francis and Josiah. I thought of those boys as the little brothers I had always wanted.

Martha began to stop us after church and ask if I could cut firewood for her. Even in the Florida heat, firewood was needed for cooking and laundry. Louise and Martha agreed on a day and I did chores and helped with her boys. I was more than glad to miss school. It didn't take long before other women stopped Louise to ask for my help.

Little news of the war came to rural Florida, but enlistment continued. In early April 1862, Milton enlisted in the Wakulla Tigers, along with pretty much all the able men remaining in the county.

On July 1, 1862, the Wakulla Tigers joined the Florida 5th Infantry at Camp Leon. There wasn't much of a celebration this time, no trick riders or drum corps to entertain us. Hard times were starting to settle in on everyone, even the August family.

Arielle's family money depended on shipping. The Union had blockades on all of the outlets near Savannah, bringing the shipping industry to a halt. The August family grew acres of cotton but, without shipping, there was no way to market the crop.

The men enlisting were paid for the use of their horses and supplies but less than before. Even the lunches changed. Instead of a basketful of chicken for each family, a table was set for the enlisting men. Louise and I tried to calm the visibly pregnant Carrie, but she cried all day.

"I won't lie to you Henry," Milton said to me. "I have a bad feeling about this war. I sure am glad you'll be here to look after things." I could see it in their faces, others had that same bad feeling.

The 3rd Florida Infantry had been gone for a year. With the Camp Leon enlistment, the county was full of women and children that needed my help. I cut firewood, mended fences, plowed gardens, and did chores for half the county, or at least it felt that way. One Sunday morning, I told Louise I just could not go to church. She laughed at me, but she understood. After church was the time most of the women approached Louise about me. Some didn't even belong to our church, but just came by to "schedule" me. So Louise let me go fishing that Sunday. I was so happy you would have thought it was Christmas.

I didn't stay happy for long. That evening, Calvin McCoy visited. I knew him by name, but he had never been to our house before. He talked about the weather for a while then he got to his point. "I hear your boy is right handy with an axe." He told Louise about the saltworks set up at Goose Creek. He went on about how salt was vital to the Confederacy. The saltworks cooked the sea water and separated the salt that could be used to preserve food for an army on the move. He explained, "Cooking the salt vats needs a steady supply of wood, and I need a boy that's good with an axe." He told Louise, "I'll be by in the morning to take Henry with me for a few days." He didn't wait for an answer, just rode off like it was a fact.

19 Salt

Before the war, salt was imported, but the Union
blockade along the coast cut off the salt shipments.
The Confederacy needed to replace the imported salt
to preserve meats and tan leather. The shallow bays
and marshes of Florida's Gulf Coast were ideal for
producing the needed preservative.

Chief and I followed McCoy to the saltworks early the next morning. I had never seen anything like it. Seawater boiled in huge pots and a large brick-drying structure had a smokestack as tall as the surrounding trees. A few small buildings stored the salt, and tents for the workers were scattered around the site. The workers boiled the salt water until it turned to mush and then spread it out on oak planks atop the brick structure to dry in the sun. In damp weather, the salt was covered, and small fires were used to help the drying process. The operation had an insatiable appetite for wood to fuel those fires.

Mules dragged the logs out of the forest to a place near the works. I spent three days, sawing and splitting the wood. At the end of each day, I was too tired to move. Blisters covered my hands, and my back felt like an old man's. I finally spoke up and said Louise was sure to need me. I gathered my things and started for home. That was when I learned there was a bonus for working at the saltworks. Salt brought a high price, and I was paid before I left. While I was in shock at the money I was paid, Mr. McCoy added that he would need me again soon.

I had never been paid cash money before. A piece of a pie or some fresh-baked bread was my regular pay. Blackberry cobbler that Martha Duncan gave me, and that I ate with her kids, was the best pay I had ever received. The jingle in my pocket took some of the pain out of my body as I headed home.

20 Tennessee to Home

The 3rd and 1st Florida Infantries pushed north toward Tennessee where they would join the Mississippi 41st under the leadership of General John C. Brown. The united group would become Brown's Brigade. When they went into camp at the foot of Lookout Mountain, the beauty left the Florida men in awe. The mountains were like nothing they had ever seen. Florida, flat as a pancake and barely above sea level, did not offer the mountain views, walls of granite, or the waterfalls that surrounded them. Thomas continued to write to us.

March 30, 1862

Dearest Louise,

Tennessee is a new world, both exciting and frightening. It is unspoken, but I feel many are wondering how they will ever find their way home.

The nights are still cold here, as is the ground. Sleeping out in the open has caused some of the men to become ill. I pray we will be home before winter.

An army on the move needs supplies. The Gulf supplies were cut off by the Union Navy and the distance. When the Union gunboats blocked the Cumberland River, our supply lines dried up. Command has been looking for other ways to gain access to much needed materials, orders, and maps. I was ordered to the Captain's Quarters.

A number of officers were studying maps when I entered. Captain Frierson shook my hand and another Captain spoke, "It has come to the attention of the command that you have traveled. I hear you can read a map and have knowledge of the rivers and roads near Atlanta."

I am proud to say they gave me an assignment. A group of us are to travel to a depot north of Atlanta to pick up necessary supplies, orders, and updated maps. Two men have already been assigned, and I must choose one of my men to go with us on the detail.

I have decided on 16-year-old Dawson Durham. Dawson is young but both a good shot and a good rider. He is a young man of quality but has a sweetheart in Aucilla and is terribly homesick. I think it will be good to give him both the responsibility and my attention.

All my love to you and Henry,

Thomas

The first time the group made the trip, things went smoothly and quickly. Thomas and his small group took custody of three pack horses and immediately returned to the camp at Lookout Mountain.

The second exchange went differently. Union troops knew the location of the supplies and they were watching. After securing the supplies, Thomas and the group started northwest back to camp. They had gone no more than a few miles when two shots rang out. Wearing the officer's uniform, Thomas fell to the ground. Dawson dismounted and dragged Thomas to cover. Thomas ordered the group to move forward while he and Dawson returned enough fire to cover their escape. The unit that had delivered the supplies heard the shots and returned, trapping the two Union snipers between them, killing both.

Thomas was bleeding heavily. Dawson did not want to leave his lieutenant, but after some discussion, he agreed he was needed with the supplies and went to join them. The soldiers that had come to their assistance took Thomas to Lawrenceville for medical care.

As an officer, he received the best care available, but that was not significant. A field hospital could be a dangerous place; instruments were not sterilized, and sanitation was poor. Thomas had been shot twice in the chest. One shot grazed his ribs, causing a fracture to the bone. The other barely missed his lung. The doctors removed the lead and assured him both wounds were relatively minor, and that he would be back with his unit in no time. The first day held promise, but then the fever set in. Within days, he was delirious and racked with chills. It wasn't long before his lungs filled with fluid.

Lawrenceville was the train depot, so the doctors made the decision to place Thomas on a train headed south; he was coming home.

The train cars were loaded with wounded, sick, and dying men. Only a few orderlies were on the train to assist the many men who needed help. Often, the most comfort they could give was a few sips of water. Though the more able men helped, the task was overwhelming. As they neared Savannah, the train was quiet; all that could be heard were a few moans and the buzz of the many flies. Thomas was sent from Savannah to Thomasville, the southernmost stop on the rail line, but still miles from home. The railroads didn't connect to Florida until after the war.

The wounded were unloaded at the Thomasville station and placed in the surrounding yards. Thomas was assigned a spot under a large oak. Shade could mean the difference between life and death in the heat.

A farmer and his wife, Joe and Anna Hanson, moved among the wounded with water and kind words. The couple had three sons and a son-in-law who had answered the call to duty. They went to the station each week looking for news about their loved ones.

Thomas could hardly speak when they gave him water. He just managed to say, "Crawfordville," and he begged the farmer to get some word to his family. The farmer and his wife loaded Thomas into their wagon and the old man set out on the Plank Road.

The Plank Road was built as a toll road, intended to provide a way for farmers from Tallahassee and Thomasville to bring their crops to the coast. The planks kept the road stable and easier to travel since Florida lacked the stone needed to "pave" a road. Along the way, Joe talked to a few travelers, and the word spread. It was pitch dark when Joe Hanson reached Newport, but a wagon was waiting for him. Ray and Clara Willis had a son-in-law in the Wakulla Guards. Joe followed them to our house.

It was close to midnight when the two wagons arrived. The old farmers helped Louise unload Thomas. Clara helped her remove his soiled uniform and unwrap the disgusting bandages. Thomas was very thin. His wounds were infected and he was delirious with fever. The women repeatedly wiped him down with cool water. Tears streamed down Louise's face as they worked.

Ray Willis left to find our neighbor, Doc Gregory. Louise told me to feed Mr. Hanson and help with his mules.

The old man said he was too tired to eat, but he was mighty worried about his mules. "Those two needed rest on the way. I guess they are as old as I am."

I brought his mules to the barn and made sure they had water and feed. I offered my bed in the loft, but Mr. Hanson refused. He would be more comfortable in the barn with his animals. I brought some blankets, and he fell asleep immediately.

The rest of the night, I was busy bringing in buckets of water and firing up the stove to boil it. I never prayed so hard in my life.

Daylight brought other wagons. Some of the women carried food. Some came for news, any news. Bowlegs arrived about noon. He had kegs of sulfur water from the springs at Newport that Daniel Lord had sent. People from all around came to the springs. They were famous as healing waters. He also had a small sack of herbs from Neea. He explained, "Neea said to boil the herbs into a tea."

Louise and I thanked him. Louise used the water to wash Thomas's wounds, and I went to make the tea.

There was little Doc could do. The war caused a shortage of even the most common medicines. Louise and I sat with Thomas for weeks. We continued to use the sulfur water to wash the wounds, damp cloths to cool his fever, and homemade plasters on his chest to help him breathe. We made the tea Neea sent and cooked broth, trying to help him get his strength back. We held his hand against the pain and prayed. By the time he began to show improvement, news had arrived from Tennessee.

Thomas had been wounded on May 8, 1862. The Army of Tennessee engaged the Union Army at Murfreesboro on May 15, 1862. The result was devastating. The Florida regiment lost a fourth of their men. When the list of dead was finally posted, the Durham boy was on it, along with the two other men assigned to the supply run. Dawson had protected Thomas and helped him hold off the snipers until help arrived. Thomas was shattered when we told him the news.

The summers in Florida are always hot, but the summer of 1862 was hotter and drier than usual. The crops suffered along with the people and animals. The flies seemed to be the only thing that prospered. Key West had rain and Yellow Fever. Everyone was afraid it would be carried here by the vessels that were able to run the blockade.

I continued to do chores for the families and cut wood for the saltworks. Meeting Jim Hill was one of the only good things about that summer. Jim also cut wood at the saltworks. He was just a few months older than I was. From Panacea, he lived closer to the Dickerson Bay Salt Works, but his dad had a falling out with their boss. All of the men in Jim's family were fishermen. Jim could clean a mullet faster than any man I knew.

We cut wood all day and at night there was fried fish or smoked fish to eat and sometimes a few oysters right out of the bay. We laid awake under the stars and talked about what we were going to do with all the money we were making.

I said, "I want to own my own land."

Jim said, "I just want to be rich enough to have someone else clean my fish."

Although Thomas was getting stronger, he was still short of breath, and truth is, he never fully recovered.

He spent most of his time in the chair under the big live oak in the front yard. A young lieutenant from the 5th Florida Cavalry, Scott's Battalion, came by a few times and sat with Thomas.

Mr. McCoy came by, too, and offered Thomas a jug for his pain. He wanted to let Thomas know how welcome he would be at the Goose Creek Salt Works. The number of men that stopped by to visit the saltworks made Louise suspect that salt wasn't the only thing they distilled at Goose Creek. I never doubted that Thomas would go with the young lieutenant.

Milton, the other members of the Wakulla Tigers, and the rest of the 5th Florida Infantry left for service in August 1862. Carrie had their first son in September. Thomas was sorry Milton wasn't there to see what a fine boy he was. We went to see her often and offered for her to stay with us, but on the first day of October, Carrie's father arrived to take her back to Georgia.

21 Molly

Mrs. Walker came by the house one afternoon at the end of October to ask for my help. She said, "My sister Molly Adams and her baby girl, Becky, are coming to stay with me for a while. They live just over the line in Jefferson County on the Pin Hook Road. Molly was expected yesterday." Mrs. Walker was sure she knew the problem. "That mule of theirs is meaner than a rattlesnake. It'll bite a hunk out of a man any time it can. Molly is scared of that mule and most likely not able to hitch the wagon."

Mrs. Walker wanted me to go to the Adams' farm and hitch up the mule for her. Jim was going fishing on the St. Marks River; I had hoped to go with him. Thomas and Louise left it up to me, but I knew what they expected. Before I left, Thomas stopped me, "A mule mean enough to bite is sure to kick. You better be mindful." I know he was thinking about Clayton. By the look on Louise's face, she was too.

Mrs. Walker added, "Henry, if you go right away, Molly can get to my house before dark."

I had to go clear to the natural bridge, where the St. Marks was kind enough to go underground, creating a convenient way to cross the river, then down the sandy Pin Hook Road. By the time I made it to the Adams' farm, I was feeling pretty sorry for myself. I had my head down, thinking about how much it hurt to be bitten by a mule, when I noticed tracks coming out from the farm.

I hoped that Molly Adams had finally hitched the mule herself, and I could still find Jim at the river. I saw by the tracks that one of the shoes on the mule was cracked on the side and needed to be replaced.

I almost turned around and started back to the river, when I saw that the Adams' mule was still in the field. I went up to the house and called out, but didn't get a response. I checked the barn and the chicken coop and finally went to the back of the house. The back door was open wide, and I could see Molly on the floor. I wanted to run but knew there was a little girl in the house. I went past Molly's body and found Becky. She had a pillow over her head, and she too was dead. I ran out of the house and rode as fast as I could toward Wacissa to get the Jefferson County sheriff.

Tears streaked my face by the time I got to Wacissa. The sheriff was out searching for Walt Hamilton, a Wakulla County man trying to avoid conscription by hiding out in the woods just over the

Jefferson County line. The old men at the store were talking about it. Hamilton kept sneaking home to gather food and see family. Normally, the family of someone evading service would be run off or burned out but Hamilton was Daniel Lord's nephew and had "connections" in Wakulla County.

One of the old men said, "I sure hope we catch him here. His connections don't mean spit here. He needs hanged and we have the rope ready."

A local went to find the sheriff for me and when he arrived, he asked me to go back to the Adams' farm with him. I waited outside while he went into the house. He wrapped Molly and Becky in quilts. I kept wiping my face so he wouldn't think I was a baby.

After he cared for the bodies, he tried to determine if anything had been taken from the house. "You see anything you think could help, boy?"

I thought for a moment. "Only those tracks." I showed him the "lightning bolt" design the broken shoe had made in the mud. We agreed the track had been made after the rain, late that night or in the morning when the ground was still soft.

It was dark by the time I got home. Thomas and Louise were frantic. Louise, worried about the mule, ran out to hug me. We both burst into tears. It was late by the time I finished telling them about Molly and the baby.

22 Lee's Army of Northern Virginia

The Wakulla Tigers, now part of fifteen hundred men who made up the 5th Florida Infantry Regiment, departed from Monticello on August 1, 1862, for service under Stonewall Jackson's command. They traveled to Virginia where they would join the Florida 2nd and 8th to become part of Lee's Army of Northern Virginia. The Florida 5th arrived just a few days before their first battle. Later, veterans would say it was a "Baptism by Fire."

On August 28, Lee's Army, consisting of forty-nine thousand men, faced Pope's Army of seventy-six thousand men at the battle of Second Manassas. Two days later, the outcome was declared a Confederate victory, but the losses were heavy on both sides. Lee lost over nine thousand men while the Union lost over sixteen thousand. The size and intensity of the conflict must have been terrifying.

September was especially unkind to the Confederates. Milton and the Florida men fought their way through Maryland. In September alone, they engaged in major battles at Frederick, Hagerstown, South Mountain, Sharpsburg, and Antietam. In each battle, the Confederate troops were greatly outnumbered. They went into battle out-supplied and usually with empty bellies. When they reached Antietam, they had fifty-two thousand men to face McClellan's seventy-five thousand.

Between September 16 and 18, the Confederates lost thirteen thousand seven hundred twenty-five men. The Union lost twelve thousand four hundred and ten, marking Antietam as a Union victory.

After each battle, the ground was littered with the dead and dying. The air was filled with the screams of tortured souls and the smell of death. Battlefield services overflowed with men that feared for their lives and feared for their souls.

Milton was wounded at Antietam and given a battlefield commission. He was recognized for courage under fire and promoted to lieutenant. Battlefield commissions did not come with celebration. They usually marked the death of an officer you had followed.

They fought for Lee at Fredericksburg on December 11. Burnside commanded one hundred fourteen thousand Union troops while the

Confederate's had seventy-two thousand. The battle was considered a Confederate victory because the Union suffered the heaviest losses, but the Confederate supplies were completely depleted.

Lee's men were hungry, outnumbered, and fatigued. Still, they rallied in May 1863 at Chancellorsville. The Union, under Hooker's command had two soldiers to every one of Lee's. I heard some of the veterans say, years later, "Our stomachs were so empty we were afraid the growling would give our positions away." Another would always add, "The horrors we saw were best seen on an empty stomach."

In July 1863, the Wakulla Tigers followed Lee to Gettysburg. At this point, the Florida 5th Infantry had taken part in the worst fighting of the war.

The screams of the dying were etched into their souls. The freshest breeze could not erase the smell of death that filled their nostrils. Their ears rang constantly from the cannon fire. The sights of the battlefield were still visible even when they closed their eyes, haunting what little sleep they could achieve.

At Gettysburg, Mead commanded eighty-three thousand Union troops, while Lee commanded seventy-five thousand Confederates, the best odds the Confederates had faced but a different circumstance. When the smoke finally cleared, fifty thousand men had lost their lives. The train cars carrying the wounded stretched on for miles.

The Florida 2nd, 5th, and 8th Infantry Regiments made up Perry's Brigade. On July 2, 1863, they were part of the attack on the center of the Union defensive line at Cemetery Ridge.

Between the Union and Confederate forces there were two hundred seventy-four cannons at Gettysburg. They produced an unimaginable horror, and a roar that could be heard for a hundred miles.

On the following day, what was left of the brigade was part of Pickett's Charge. The Confederates advanced arm-to-arm in close formation, showing discipline, brotherhood, and dedication. A "sea of grey" moved as one, shoulder-to-shoulder toward the Union cannons. No one can doubt the courage it took to stay in formation when hell fire was all around. The Florida Infantry fought so fiercely, they drove beyond the line and were trapped when others pulled back. Large numbers of the Florida Infantry were either killed or taken prisoner. Seven hundred seventeen Florida men went into the battle; four hundred fifty-five perished. Milton was badly wounded. He took a bullet to his lower jaw.

So many were in need after the battle that a Confederate prisoner was not a priority. In agonizing pain, Milton was finally sent to Letterman General

Hospital, a large field hospital near Gettysburg. There was little they could do. Milton's lower jaw was shattered, and a few teeth were broken. Opening or closing his mouth caused excruciating pain. The surgeon sewed the wound and reinforced the jaw as best he could. He gave Milton a few reeds to act as a straw so he could at least have water. Milton was transferred to Fort Henry in Baltimore and then to Point Lookout where he would join the rest of the captured Florida men as a prisoner of war.

Milton was as weak as a kitten by the time he arrived at Point Lookout. His eyes filled with tears when he saw the first Florida man.

23 Roscoe

Archie Moore's family had a farm near the Sopchoppy River in Wakulla County. He was a hog farmer and always had a kind word to say about Dooly. Archie enlisted in the 2nd Florida Infantry and he was as fine a warrior as his father's Scotland could produce, strong and determined. He also received a field commission as a lieutenant.

The Florida men sought out each other at the battle of Second Manassas. A group of them, including Archie, huddled around Milton, the day Milton met Roscoe.

Archie dipped a small piece of bread into his cup of gruel to moisten it. He rolled it into small balls with his own filthy hands, helping Milton to eat.

Roscoe took one look at Milton and laughed. "Don't look like you going to be givin' orders now, Mr. Lieutenant. No sir, no orders. Old Roscoe isn't going to worry about you. You dead already. You just don't know it." Roscoe let out a large laugh that rang with madness.

Born a slave, Roscoe's back was crisscrossed with the evidence of abuse he had suffered. The Union had freed Roscoe, and his position as a guard gave him power. The sudden gift of life and death over the men in his care gave him a vehicle for revenge and created a monster.

Officers were the victims of Roscoe's most sadistic abuse. Roscoe delivered beatings without mercy; he beat some to death. He prided himself on his ability to humiliate the men. The camp water supply was polluted, causing hundreds of men to have violent diarrhea. Roscoe blocked the privies at night, compelling the men, at the point of a bayonet, to march in double quick time, carry him on their backs, or kneel and pray to Abe Lincoln before they could have entrance. He howled with laughter when his victims were pushed beyond their limits, soiling themselves.

Archie had tried to talk to Roscoe. He told him he was from a poor, rural community and had never owned a slave. "My father came to this country as an indentured servant. All I want is to keep from being one myself."

Roscoe had considered this for a minute and then spit on the ground. "I sure am glad you shared that with me. I've been thinking that swamp you from is too far for anyone to come here or make a fuss. I could smoke you swamp rats without a worry. Now that I know you're just poor dirt farmers that wouldn't be missed, I'm sure nobody'll care when I kill you. No, sir. No one is going to bother Roscoe about the likes of you swamp rats."

"The bottom rail is on top now," Roscoe told the group. "You better be careful." He looked at Archie. "My gun has been wanting to smoke you all day!" He wandered off a couple of steps, then turned and pointed his finger with his thumb raised to resemble a gun. He waved it at all of them, "None of you swamp rats are ever going to see home again."

Archie started to step forward but Milton reached out and grabbed his friend's ankle.

The veterans would say, Roscoe left with a grin on his face.

24 Protecting the Coast

THE WAR IN FLORIDA—THE CREW OF THE U. S. STEAMER CLERS AND SUIPER, IN THE CAPTURED SCHOONER CAROLINA SURVIVING, AT OCHLOCKONY RIVER, ENGAGING THE DISMOUNTED REBEL CAVALRY ON SHORE.—FROM A SKETCH BY PAYMASTER JOHN J. PRATT, U. S. N.

When Thomas recovered, he enlisted in the Florida 5th Cavalry. He joined the young lieutenant who had visited with him under the live oak so many times. The entire state was on alert. Tallahassee didn't have any military value, but as the capital of a

Confederate state, it was a target. The local men patrolled the coastline, looking for signs of invasion. It wasn't long before the Union made its appearance on the coast.

The ports of St. Marks and Newport were crucial to defending Tallahassee. They provided a supply route in and out of North Florida, moving cotton and essential supplies such as salt and the shot or bullets that the foundry produced. The Union Navy blockaded St. Marks at the first of the war. Wakulla's many rivers, bays, and saltmarshes provided cover for blockade runners. The quick little *Spray*, now called the CSS *Spray*, was equipped with two cannons, so she was the blockade-running star for the region.

In March 1863, armed Union boats sailed up the Ochlockonee River in an attempt to capture Confederate vessels, including the CSS *Onward*. The Confederate sloop was loaded with salt, cotton, and ammunition. The *Onward* was captured and towed down the river by the Union Navy. The 5th Florida Cavalry under Captain George Washington Scott heard the news and raced to defend the sloop. Scott's men, including Thomas, fired on the boats, using the tree-lined river banks to hide their positions. The boats had no cover and were vulnerable even though their artillery out-gunned the Confederates. The Union soldiers must have thought every tree on the river bank had a Reb behind it. They finally released the *Onward* and made way. The Union left, with one man dead and six wounded. Scott's company had no casualties.

The Spanish built San Marcos de Apalache, a stone fort, at the confluence of the Wakulla and St. Marks rivers. The Confederates occupied the fort, adding artillery batteries and renaming it Fort Ward. The fort provided security for the ports, the foundry at Newport, and the mills in the area. It could also provide security for the *Spray* on its runs.

The lighthouse at St. Marks was a Confederate lookout. The lens from the lighthouse was removed to protect it, but the height and location provided an excellent view of the Gulf. In July 1863, a lookout at the lighthouse was the first to sight the Union Navy. An expedition in small boats was trying to travel up the St. Marks River to capture Fort Ward and the *Spray*. Word spread quickly, and the Confederates were able to fire on the vulnerable, small boats, forcing the Union troops to withdraw. The Union moved out, but not before they inflicted damage on the lighthouse. It had been shelled the year before, and the Union soldiers shelled it again, but they also came ashore to burn the wooden steps, making the lighthouse unusable as a lookout.

About the same time, a federal detachment from the gunboat USS *Port Royal* attacked the saltworks near St. George's Sound. Six boilers, two large vats, and several kettles were destroyed.

Early in the war, the USS *Kingfisher* attacked the works at St. Joseph's Bay. The *Kingfisher* gave the men a two-hour warning before destroying the site. The Confederates used that time to move as much of the processed salt as possible. The Union never gave another warning. Two men were killed at St. George and a few were burned by scalding water, one critically.

The Goose Creek Salt Works, was not far from the lighthouse. To make up for the salt lost during the raids, we had to step up our output. We were always on guard. A clear night was particularly dangerous. The glow from the fires could be seen for miles, luring the Union vessels in.

There were no major ports along our coastline. The series of small ports meant the blockade vessels had to patrol a whole sector rather than a single station. The blockade vessels could be tracked from the coast, creating opportunities for small vessels hiding in the many rivers and inlets to run the blockade.

The CSS Schooner *Caroline Gertrude* was one of the vessels that frequently ran the blockade. At the last of December 1863, she held a load of cotton ready to export when her captain and crew misjudged the shallow bay. She ran aground on an oyster bar in Ochlockonee Bay. The USS *Stars and Stripes* made an attempt to capture the stranded vessel. The 5th Florida Cavalry again set up behind cover and pelted the *Stars and Stripes* with musket fire. After a few hours, the tide began to turn. The Union vessel feared being trapped in the shallow bay, so they set fire to the *Caroline Gertrude* and made a hasty retreat, carrying her crew as prisoners.

25 Tracks

There had been a few whispers among the ladies after church about a young girl near the Suwannee River and two sisters near the coast in Taylor County, all found dead. After I discovered Molly and Becky Adams, the whispers grew into real fear. Walt Hamilton, Daniel Lord's nephew, was a suspect in Molly's murder because he was known to be hiding in the area at that time. The woods hid the occasional runaway slave and others drawn to the port, not the kind you could trust. All of them were considered dangerous. At least one was guilty of murder.

I was still making good money cutting wood for the saltworks, but they stopped paying in gold coin and started to give us Confederate currency. I sure missed the jingle of those coins.

Jim's dad, Fred Hill, was a moonshiner and a drunk. Conscription laws required all men to join the military. Producing salt was considered so important, it exempted a man from service. Jim's dad worked distilling salt during the day and moonshine at night.

Jim told me a story about him. "He came home so drunk, that his own dog bit him."

I immediately wanted to know what happened to the dog.

"It licked my dad awake in the morning, and all was forgiven. He even bragged about what a good watchdog he was."

The nicest thing I can say about Jim's dad is he didn't hit those he loved, but he did threaten to thump Jim if he caught him with a jug. Fred Hill was the size of a mountain and known as a scrapper. Most of the men at the Goose Creek Salt Works tried to stay on his good side and refused to give me or Jim even a pull on their jug.

A scraggly looking fellow showed up at Goose Creek just about breakfast time one morning. Earl said he had been working at the saltworks in Dixie County until the USS *Stars and Stripes* "blew her to hell." Mr. McCoy listened to his story then told him he would have to start at the bottom, cutting wood with Jim and me.

Earl chewed tobacco all day long. The few teeth he had were brown and nasty. He had a wild look to him that I didn't take to.

At the end of the day, Earl invited us to his campsite just beyond the woods. He had a jug and was willing to share. I didn't want to go.

I told Jim, "I can't drink after that man."

Jim called me a "big baby." He grabbed a cup and told me to come on.

We walked just beyond the tree line to Earl's camp. As Jim and I stood around talking to Earl, Jim filled his cup and passed it between us. That was when I saw the "lightning bolt" tracks. I don't know if it was the drink or the thought of Molly, but I was instantly sick to my stomach.

I made a dumb excuse about Louise needing me and headed straight to Wacissa to find Sheriff Johnson.

26 The Battle of Olustee

Tallahassee was chosen as the Capital site in part because it was halfway between Florida's two principal cities, St. Augustine and Pensacola. At one time, the legislature alternated sessions between the two cities. Travel was difficult and the trip was twenty days long, making it an unsatisfactory arrangement. The story is that each city sent a rider toward the other city and the riders eventually met in Tallahassee, a satisfactory midpoint for the new Capital.

Early in the war, the Union troops occupied Fort Pickens in Pensacola and Fort Taylor in Key West. About the time the 3rd Florida Infantry was experiencing heavy losses in Tennessee, the Union occupied Fernandina Beach and St. Augustine. The Union threatened Jacksonville from the start of the war. Most thought it was only a matter of time before they moved on Tallahassee.

141

The 5th Florida Cavalry became the primary guard for the Capital. They patrolled the coast to protect Tallahassee from invasion. They were always on guard, for threats of fire or assassination plots. When the fear of a Union push increased the need to protect the Capital, Thomas was assigned to Tallahassee.

The Capital patrol was Thomas's introduction to state politics. His guard position gave him an inside look at the workings of the Capitol. A number of the representatives and senators stayed in Tallahassee even when there were no sessions to keep them there. Travel was difficult and some considered Tallahassee safer than their own towns.

Thomas had a chance to watch them and the experience marked him. He was impressed with some and disgusted by others. Most were wealthy men, born with privilege. Some felt entitled to profit from the sweat and blood of their slaves; they would do anything to keep their wealth, even if it meant spilling the blood of their poorer neighbors, men who had never owned a slave.

The Confederate Congress passed conscription laws requiring all males eighteen to thirty-five to serve in the military. They would have no option but to fight; to refuse could have devastating results. Coal oil was used to poison wells, homes were burned, and men hanged for such offenses.

In February 1864, the Union made a push from Jacksonville in an effort to take control of the Capital and to disrupt the supplies Florida was providing to the Confederate troops. A Union force of about five thousand men marched west from Jacksonville. The Confederates mustered every man they could and met the Union troops at Olustee near Lake City.

The battle was particularly fierce. The Confederate forces had a lot at stake. At one point, they charged and captured many Union artillery pieces. I imagine the men I would later see, still on the Lloyd station platform, were some who made the charge.

With control of the artillery, the Confederates threatened to flank the Union Infantry. The 35th US Colored Infantry provided cover for the Union withdrawal. The battle was considered a Confederate victory, but at a high cost.

A number of wounded were placed on the train at Lake City, headed west. The Florida railroads did not connect to Georgia. The Florida, Atlantic and Gulf Central Railroad ran across north Florida from Jacksonville to Lake City. The Pensacola and Georgia Railroad ran from Lake City to near Quincy.

When the train stopped at the little depot in Lloyd, a number of women waited. They had water and bandages ready to give the wounded men some relief. An officer in charge made the decision to unload a number of the seriously wounded men leaving them in the women's care.

27 Earl

I hadn't wanted to go to Earl's camp. Louise would be some kind of mad if she caught me drinking. I should have listened to that little voice inside of me that knew it was not the right thing to do.

When I arrived in Wacissa, I was told the sheriff, Eli Johnson, was in Lloyd. Johnson, along with most any able man, had spent the day at the station helping the women take their new charges out of the Florida sun into their homes for care. It was dark before I arrived at the depot in Lloyd, but every lantern in the town was lit.

LLOYD RAILROAD STATION

The wounded men had been moved. The dead were the only soldiers still at the station. Slaves from a nearby plantation washed the blood from the depot platform as the women talked with the sheriff about where to bury the unfortunate men. One of them told the sheriff, "We want these men to be cared for in the morning. The Bond family has agreed to have them buried at their cemetery. It's close to the depot."

During the war, one of the great sorrows families of lost men faced was the fact that their loved ones were so far away in graves they would never see. The women wanted these men to be buried with a family, if not their own.

When the sheriff finished helping the women, he spotted me. I quickly told him my story. "I saw the tracks." I said.

"The tracks we saw at the Adams' farm?" he asked.

"I've seen the mule with the broken shoe," I told him.

He hesitated. "Are you sure, boy?"

I knew he was needed here in Lloyd, but I was sure. "Yes sir."

"Who owns the mule?" he asked.

I told him about Earl. "He says he's from Dixie County, down by the Suwanee. He told Mr. McCoy he worked the saltworks there until it was attacked."

I could still see he was torn by his duty here and going with me. "Does he chew?" he finally asked.

I grinned as I answered, "All day long."

Evidently, he had seen wads of tobacco near the bodies. I had been too terrified to notice.

By now, it was very late. I had cut wood all day and then traveled on the dusty roads to Lloyd. Sheriff Johnson invited me to his home for the night. I asked to sleep in the barn with Chief and fell asleep immediately.

Early in the morning, we went to the Bond Family Cemetery for the burials, then we headed to the Goose Creek Salt Works.

Jim and Earl were splitting logs when we arrived. Sheriff Johnson went to talk to Mr. McCoy.

Jim wanted to know, "Where did you go in such a hurry?" He told me he had not stayed at Earl's camp for long. He sheepishly admitted to spending time "puking his guts out." Earl kept giving me a hard look. He didn't like seeing me arrive with the sheriff.

Mr. McCoy finally told Jim's dad, "Fred, you keep an eye on Earl for me." Fred already suspected Earl had given his boy a jug. Earl didn't move. McCoy and Sheriff Johnson went to check the mule tracks. Sure enough, the mule's cracked shoe left a track that looked like a lightning bolt. The two men searched Earl's belongings.

Sheriff Johnson found a silver hair clip that had been missing from the body of a young girl who had lived near the Suwanee River. He found two rings that belonged to the sisters from Taylor County and a locket that belonged to Molly Adams. The locket still held a lock of Becky's hair. Sheriff Johnson also discovered a small, gold cross. He had no way to know who had owned the gold cross, but he was pretty sure it meant another woman was dead.

The Wakulla County Sheriff arrived before noon. Earl could have been tried by his peers at the Goose Creek Salt Works and hanged that evening. Mr. McCoy and the others would have been willing, but there was political value to solving Molly's murder. The two sheriffs and a deputy took Earl back to Monticello for trial.

Jim and I never took to drink. Drinking with a murderer was more than either of us had bargained for.

28 Tightening the Noose on Tallahassee

In April 1864, federal troops from the USS *Restless* landed with orders to proceed to East Bay. Their main target was the large saltworks at East Bay, but they had orders to capture any Confederate vessels anchored in the area. Two large saltworks were lost, along with three hundred bushels of salt.

In May, Union soldiers from the schooner *Fox* destroyed a number of saltworks between the Suwannee River and St. Marks. Twenty-five kettles and one hundred bushels of salt were destroyed. Each attack on the saltworks had a story of a man scalded by the pots of boiling salt water.

In September 1864, the Union tried again to tighten the noose on Tallahassee. This time, a Union force of about seven hundred men came from the west, from their base in Pensacola, under the command of Brigadier General Asboth. They conducted a raid deep into West Florida toward Marianna.

Marianna was important as a trade center and the rich soil in Jackson County provided needed food supplies. Marianna was also a Confederate military base with a training center, hospital, storehouses, and stables.

The Confederate militia fought fiercely to keep their town from Union hands. When the battle was over, parts of the town were burned, ten Confederates were dead and sixteen wounded. The Union took forty men as prisoners.

General Asboth was severely wounded, taking shot to his arm and face. Confederate reinforcements were organized and descended on Marianna the next day, but they found the Union forces had taken their wounded leader and retreated to Pensacola.

29 A Different Enemy

With so many attacks, McCoy expected Jim and me to work round the clock. I was late getting there the day the storm hit. I was worried McCoy would be mad.

Mrs. Potter had asked Louise for my help that morning. A sow hog and a litter of piglets trampled her garden. Normally, a hog that damaged a garden would find its way to the smokehouse, but she wanted the piglets. She asked me and Dooly to catch the offending swine and pen her up; the piglets would come to their mama. Mrs. Potter also needed me to notch their ears and neuter the young males. I told the little guys I would do my best by them.

When I finished with the pigs, I had to take Dooly home. He stayed with Louise for protection when she was alone. It was late afternoon before I got to the saltworks.

I was prepared for Mr. McCoy's usual speech about me wanting the work or not, but he was deep in conversation with one of the fishermen. The man had skin as brown and tough as leather. The two talked about the dark clouds that were gathering. The fisherman had tied his boat up and loaded his nets into his wagon. On his way out, he told Jim and me, "Its best you all go home." McCoy had other ideas.

He had us load salt bags on a wagon headed toward Tallahassee. Each bag weighed about fifty pounds and there must have been fifty of them. We covered the bags with a tarp and sent off the wagon just before the wind picked up. Jim and I headed to our tent. The fisherman had left us fresh mullet and Jim's dad had it ready to cook. We were eating when the rain started.

Within an hour, the rain was coming in torrents. The wind tried to pick up our tent. Trees fell and waves slapped the coast. Then we heard a sound none of us had ever heard before, or since, a roar so loud I was sure the "hounds of hell" were coming for us. Sailors talked about giant waves, taller than the tallest trees. I never imagined I would witness one. A wall of water washed us from our tent and sent everything flying inland. I grabbed a tree limb to keep from being tossed about like a piece of driftwood. I hung on for dear life. Lightning cracked all around, terrifying me to the bone.

The Gulf of Mexico had pitched a huge "tantrum," but in the morning, the sun came out as if everything was just fine. Jim was hanging onto a branch near the top of an old live oak tree, and I hung onto one on the other side. Not long after daylight, a small boat came by looking for us. They loaded us into the boat, and Jim called for his dad. There was no answer.

Louise was frantic by the time I got home. Chief had come home without me, sending her into a panic.

The storm destroyed two saltworks operations and twenty-five lives, six at Goose Creek and nineteen at Dickerson Bay. Jim's dad and Mr. McCoy were among the dead.

Months later, when the water receded, I went back to the live oak that had saved Jim and me. Sitting on Chief, the watermark from the ground up was over our heads.

The storm had knocked down trees and damaged roofs. Half of the ladies in the county had a tree on a fence or a roof that leaked, if they still had a roof. I had lost my job at the saltworks but gained a long list of chores.

There was another result from the storm: Bowlegs had disappeared. Some said he drowned.

He had been increasingly unhappy. Confederate soldiers had taken over the *Spray* and the foundry, so Bowlegs had found himself back where he started, loading and unloading vessels.

As a boy, he'd been a slave on the waterfront in Charleston. Daniel Lord always had an eye for a bargain and he needed that kind of help in Florida. He saw the young man work and decided he was a slave he wanted. Lord negotiated the sale and Bowlegs earned his name.

Before the storm, he was taking orders from men who didn't have a fraction of his experience. Lincoln had freed the slaves, but the soldiers and sailors at Newport didn't seem to know anything about it.

Bowlegs was smart. The chaos after the storm would give days of cover for a man on the run. As far as I know, no one in Wakulla County ever saw Bowlegs or Neea again.

30 Santa Claus

I worked for two days, patching leaks on Angus Moore's roof. I told Louise, "That old man sure is hard to please." I came home in such a bad mood that Louise suggested I go to Panacea and check on Jim. I hadn't been to Panacea since his dad's funeral and I really wanted to go.

I stayed with my friend for two nights. Fred Hill had built the house with a beautiful view of Dickerson Bay. The salt air had scoured the whitewash away years ago; the shutters were crooked, and the front porch leaned badly. Jim didn't seem bothered by the need for repairs.

Jim and I pulled the seine net each morning, catching a boatload of mullet. We spent the afternoon cleaning the fish, salting and placing it in the smokehouse. At night, we made a fire on the beach, sat around it, and told stories about the saltworks. We howled with laughter when Jim retold the story about his dad coming home so drunk his own dog didn't recognize him. We smoked our catch and watched the stars late into the night.

In the morning, we wrapped the smoked mullet in oilskins and headed to the fish market in Panacea. On the way to the market, we passed a family of former slaves living in the woods. It didn't look like they had much of anything. One of their boys was about our age. He was tall and reed thin. We heard his mother call him "Bug."

At the market, vendors wanted to buy our mullet, but they wanted to pay us in Confederate dollars. Jim and I decided that to trade the fish for Confederate money was the same as giving it away. I wrapped some of the mullet for Louise and me, and we gave the rest to families in need, including the family in the woods. Jim said it made him feel just like "Santa Claus."

The little family was doing their best to survive. The land they camped on belonged to Malcolm Davis. The old man had lost his two sons at Antietam and the loss nearly killed him. After a particularly bad day, Davis took his shotgun and headed to the woods to rid himself of the intruders. He rode to the woods, cocked the shotgun, and pointed it at the former slaves. Bug's father, Nathan, stood in front of Rose and the children with empty hands, willing to give his life to protect them. The old man looked at the family and scanned their small camp. Shame washed over him. He crumpled to the ground, talking to ghosts, lost in pain.

Nathan helped the old man mount his horse and walked it home. He helped Malcolm to the door but did not enter. Nathan swept the porch with a broom that was propped against the doorjamb and stacked the firewood scattered in the yard. After that, Nathan paid rent. He showed up every few days to look in on the old man and to do chores for his new landlord.

I hadn't been home from Panacea for very long when Sheriff Johnson came by the house. I was needed to testify at Earl's trial a week from Monday. He wanted me to come to Monticello for the trial. I showed him the mullet and invited him to dinner. "My wife needs me at home," he said. "And I hope to get there before dark." He did take a few smoked mullet with him. Before he rode out, he stopped me. "Don't you boys enlist before this trial. I need your testimony. You don't want that man killing more."

Jim and I had spent that morning working out a plan to enlist. I was fourteen and Jim almost fifteen. The work at the saltworks had counted as service, but that was gone. Everyone our age enlisted.

31 Justice

Sheriff Johnson's wife was a really nice lady. Before the trial, she made a special breakfast of biscuits, grits, and ham. Most families were lucky to have grits.

The Johnson's grandchildren lived with them. Their son-in-law had been a member of the Jefferson Rifles. He had enlisted in the 3rd Florida Infantry like Thomas. He was on the casualty list after the second battle of Murfreesboro. Their oldest daughter had died a few months before, when her appendix burst, killing her within days, so their three sons were now with the Johnsons. While I was there, they put the youngest boy in with his brother, and I slept in his bed.

In my lifetime, there would be a new courthouse in Monticello, with a dome, huge columns, and clocks facing each direction. It would sit on a rise and be the centerpiece of the town, but the old courthouse where the trial was held was a whitewashed wooden building that was often mistaken for a church.

The day of the trial, it had a full "congregation." When I arrived at the courthouse, none of the seats were empty. Even a reporter from the local paper was there.

Sheriff Johnson had gotten statements from the sheriff in Taylor County and from the mother of a young girl found along the Suwanee. He had expected Mr. McCoy to testify, but I was the main witness now.

"There are a few questions you're sure to be asked," Johnson told me. "Just tell them the story as simply as you can and you'll be all right. Tell the truth no matter what."

The prosecutor was the first to question me. He led me through the details about the tracks, going to Wacissa to get Sheriff Johnson, and finally, seeing the tracks again.

Then it was the defense attorney's turn. He asked his first question. "Henry, do you have a girlfriend?"

"No sir," I replied.

"But you would like one, wouldn't you?" he asked.

My face turned a little red. I didn't know what to say. Finally, I answered, "I guess so."

"You were the first to know Molly was dead, weren't you?" he asked.

I gave a weak, "Yes, sir."

"Why were you at Earl's camp?" He knew I would have trouble letting everyone know about Earl's jug.

My face turned a deeper shade of red. I didn't answer.

The judge said, "You need to answer, son."

Earl had a smirk on his face, and he seemed to be laughing at me. I remembered what Sheriff Johnson said, and I blurted out, "We went to Earl's to drink." My face was beet red, and I was so glad Louise wasn't there. A few people laughed. The man from the *Monticello Family Friend*, the local newspaper, kept writing, making me even more embarrassed.

The defense's next question was, "These tracks you *say* you saw, how sure were you that they were the same tracks, months after you supposedly saw them the first time?"

I was mad by now. "Sure enough to ride all the way to Lloyd," I said. That got a big laugh.

"You admit you were at the camp where the items were found. You admit you were the first to know Molly was dead. You admit you want female company and that you indulge in drink. Aren't you a better suspect than this hard-working man here?" He placed his hand on Earl's shoulder.

I sat there too mad to answer. Before the judge could push me to speak, the defense rested. Earl kept grinning at me. I got so upset the tips of my ears felt hot.

The trial only lasted two days. The jury convicted Earl and sentenced him to hang. Sheriff Johnson was the first to shake my hand, followed by the prosecutor and a line of people I didn't know. Everyone told me how grateful they were Earl would no longer be a danger to womenfolk. Mrs. Walker gave me a tearful hug.

32 Atlanta

Any happiness over Earl's conviction was overshadowed by the news of Atlanta. The Union army lead by William T. Sherman was closing in on the city. The Union troops were burning everything in their path. The skies above Georgia were as red as the earth beneath. The Confederate Army of Tennessee, including the 3rd Florida Infantry, had been pushed back from Tennessee and were now in place to defend Atlanta. There was a real concern that if Atlanta fell, we could be next.

The 3rd Florida Infantry was rumored to be eating acorns; they had nothing else.

The trickle of news said the Confederate forces lost the Battle of Kennesaw Mountain but managed to hold the Union troops back for nearly a month. Sherman's men were finally able to break through their lines and Atlanta became an inferno.

After Atlanta, Sherman's troops headed toward Milledgeville, Georgia's State Capital, causing great alarm in Tallahassee. In the end, Sherman's men turned to Savannah and marched to the sea, cutting a swath of destruction.

The Union Army of Tennessee was in a frenzy by the time they pushed north into South Carolina. The reports said they unleased their fury, taking particular pleasure in punishing "the nest where secession was hatched."

33 Our Final Battle

The longer the war lasted, the longer it took for news to filter down to rural Florida. Every time it did, the number of widows grew.

Some of the only good news concerned Milton. A letter came saying he had been transferred to the Invalid Corp.

The men at Point Lookout slept on the ground, rations were small and the water foul. Men died daily. The camp commander was under pressure to lower the death rate so he transferred out the men he thought wouldn't make it through the Maryland winter, the war was over for the men assigned to the Invalid Corp. They would help Milton go home to Carrie in Coweta County.

The day I told Louise I had enlisted in the local militia, I noticed how tired and thin she had gotten. Jim and I enlisted in January 1865.

This New Year didn't bring much to celebrate. I still remember how exciting it had been when

Thomas enlisted. The trick riders, music, and chicken baskets made the day like a fair.

When Jim and I enlisted, we didn't even get uniforms. Jim had his dad's cap and I sure wanted one. "Don't we at least get a cap?" I asked.

The sergeant and the men around him had a good laugh. He finally told us, "You two get going now."

We were assigned to be part of the coastal watch. We were to ride the coast and riverbanks looking for the enemy.

Only a few places off the Gulf coast were deep enough for larger vessels to navigate. The Apalachicola River is a wide navigable river, and it was the next target. Word came in January that a Union gunboat was spotted in the Apalachicola. The Confederates had six cannons in place along the river near Rico's Bluff and the 5th Florida Cavalry set up along the riverbanks to support the artillery. The gunboat was heavily armed, but the Confederates had cover, it didn't take long for the Union vessel to head back to sea.

On the first of March 1865, a flotilla of Union vessels came to the entrance of the St. Marks River. Jim and I, along with half the people on the coast, spotted it. The flotilla was hard to miss. It consisted of nine blockade ships and a number of transport vessels.

For two days, the Union vessels attempted to ascend the shallow St. Marks River unsuccessfully. They finally gave up on the river assault and landed the troops near the lighthouse. They traveled inland and attacked Newport. They attempted to cross the St. Marks using the bridge at Newport, but the Confederates had time to organize a defense. The 5th Florida Cavalry tore out a section of the bridge to keep the enemy from crossing. Jim and I were at the bridge along with the rest of the local militia. We had cover and were able to hold the bridge for hours. The March day was cool, but every part of me was sweating, every nerve tingling. When the Union troops tried to breech the damage to the bridge, it became evident we could not hold them back and orders came to burn the bridge.

The Union had to cross the river to attack Tallahassee. This knowledge gave us a real advantage. Without the bridge at Newport, the best place to cross was a natural bridge six miles upriver. Before the Newport Bridge was set on fire, Jim and I were sent to Natural Bridge.

Our sergeant called to us before we left, "We need to keep them from crossing the river. Do you think you can put some trees down to give us cover?"

Jim and I carried axes on our saddles from our days at the saltworks and had cut, or had seen others cut, so many trees that we could put one down exactly where we wanted it to land. We could judge the top weight and knew which direction it would fall. I assured him we could and set out to Natural Bridge. A few members of the 5th Cavalry, Scott's Brigade, were at the crossing when we got there. With their help, we placed our trees to form a breastwork. A local militia from Gadsden County came behind us, helping to place the cannons and adding reinforcement to the breastwork.

News of the Union landing electrified Tallahassee. Telegrams were sent to call troops from all across North Florida. Confederate reinforcements continued to arrive. Our defenders included infantry reserves, regular artillery, cavalry units, various militia groups, and the cadets from the West Florida Seminary in Tallahassee. The cadets were just boys.

When the rest of the 5th Florida Cavalry arrived, I found Thomas.

There was a flurry of activity. The cannons needed to be secured, the animals moved to safety, and the breastwork was constantly being reinforced. There was motion until well after dark. Sleep was out of the question. My mind kept going to the battle at the Newport Bridge and hoping I would have the courage to face the enemy in the morning.

The Union troops arrived at daybreak on March 6, 1865. They found our forces already in place, including artillery. Jim and I fought next to Thomas. As soon as the firing started, the air filled with smoke, the roar of the cannons, and the screams of the unfortunate. The Union forces made several attempts to cross the bridge, but we had six cannons to their three, the high ground, and the breastworks. We also had a determination to defend our Capital.

Unable to cross the river, the Union troops retreated to the coast. Union casualties totaled twenty-one dead, eighty-nine wounded, and thirty-eight captured. Our force suffered three killed and at least twenty-three wounded.

The victory at Natural Bridge kept Tallahassee in Confederate hands until the end of the war.

After the Union withdrawal, our sergeant threw me his grey uniform "reb" cap. "Henry, you earned this," he said. I wore that cap until it literally fell apart.

The war was all but over, so many lives were lost, and it was too much for our governor to bear. Florida's Governor John Milton died at his own hand on April 1, 1865.

In Virginia, Grant's army cut off Lee's retreat at the Battle of Appomattox Court House. Lee was forced to surrender on April 9, 1865. The Army of Northern Virginia was officially disbanded, and the Confederate men were paroled three days later.

Florida surrendered her undefeated Capitol in May. Thomas, Jim, and I were safe, but we never saw many of our neighbors again.

The CSS *Spray*, having outrun dozens of Union vessels, was one of the last surrenders. The *Spray* surrendered at Fort Ward on May 12, 1865. Our war was over just a few days from my fifteenth birthday.

I planned on celebrating the end of the war and my birthday with Jim. We were going to have oysters and shrimp, sit next to a fire, and find the brightest stars in the sky. That was the plan, before I lost Dooly. He'd been slowing down for a while. Then one morning, he just didn't wake up. Jim and I still got together and we ate oysters and shrimp, but the stars didn't look all that bright.

34 Surviving Peace

When Lee surrendered, the 5th Florida Infantry consisted of forty-seven men and six officers. They were all that remained from the fifteen hundred men who left Monticello. Our small communities were decimated, the children all sad-eyed, and the women frantic.

There were so many women in mourning that store-dyed, black material was impossible to find, and the women had to dye their own dresses. After a few washes, the dresses faded to a variety of depressing hues.

Confederate soldiers who survived the war still had to travel home. The men who were imprisoned with Milton at Point Lookout had a journey of over one thousand miles. They had the rags on their back and little else to help them. The veterans arrived in Florida scarecrow thin, close to starvation. All had wounds, some that showed right away, and some that didn't until you talked a while.

I was a veteran and had earned the rights to hear the stories the returning veterans told. After Atlanta, Sherman asked, "Why did men that had never owned a slave fight so hard?" He was told they were promised a slave.

Recalling that later always got big laughs from the veterans. Everyone would slap a knee or bend in two with laughter. One of the veterans would ask, "You think Sherman would charge a cannon for a promise?"

None of them would. Things always got quiet after. Each man had to come to grips with the "why."

The truth was they were Americans before they were soldiers. They fought next to their family, friends, and neighbors. Not fighting their hardest would be unthinkable.

Newport was one of the communities that dwindled to a shadow of its former self. We had burned the bridge and the foundry to keep them out of Union hands. Without them and missing a large part of the population, Newport all but disappeared.

Northern industries prospered during the war. Men we called "carpetbaggers" came south with their pockets full, ready to pounce on our misfortune, grabbing land for the taxes owed. Our Confederate dollars were useless, leaving few resources. Families that had fought hard to carve out a home in the Florida wilderness were left homeless and hopeless.

Lincoln had been hated in the south. It was ironic that our best hope for mercy died with him.

Turkey buzzards migrate and traditionally winter near the headwaters of the Wakulla River. Vultures of all kinds thrived during the war. In the winter of 1865, turkey buzzards filled the branches of the spreading oaks in North Florida. It was particularly ominous, like everything was coming to "pick our bones."

35 Tears Rain on Georgia

Early December is an important time for cotton gins in North Florida, but there was very little cotton compared to before the war. The cotton that was ginned was the only hope for income that the growers and Thomas had. Thomas and I worked hard to get the cotton ginned and baled.

Our letter from Milton was one of the only bright spots during that time. Milton and Carrie welcomed a new son at the first of December. While Thomas and I worked, Thomas kept talking about Milton. He called Milton "a sly old dog" at least a fifty times, always with a grin on his face. Milton, nearly starved and disfigured, had produced a fine son in record time.

There was a second letter after the first of the year, this one from Carrie. Her father was ill. Milton was unable to farm but his work for Daniel Lord helped him find a job as a clerk for Coweta County.

He had just started the job, and his pay was small. They owed taxes on the land they couldn't pay. Milton was too proud to ask, but Carrie was desperate.

That was when Thomas started to sell off his land.

I still had some gold from the saltworks. Thomas wanted me to have my own land. He said I needed to plan for my own family. We walked around the land and talked about the fields and high ridges where the farming would be best, but it was the woods and swampy land that I wanted. I needed the lumber they offered.

I fished with Jim every chance I got. Jim supported his family with the fish we sold, but we always found some to give away. We would pull the seine net all day and, at night, we would sit by the fire and stare at the stars. We talked about owning a sawmill and how rich we were going to be.

When Thomas sold the first parcels of land, we went to the bank and had a letter of credit drawn up. Thomas and I were going to take a trip to Georgia.

The war had been over for almost a year, but the roads were still a dangerous place. Sherman saw to it the railroads had miles without track. Rail travel was impossible.

Throughout Georgia, camps of desperate men huddled around fires in the February cold. Some were Union deserters unable to go home. Some were Confederates who no longer had homes. Groups of former slaves gathered around the fires, too, unsure where home was.

We went first to Dooly County and family. Two of Thomas's nephews traveled with us to Coweta. Four armed men were safer than two. Both were hardened veterans anxious to earn the money Thomas would pay. The older nephew, Daniel, had damage to his left arm from a shot he had taken in the shoulder. He could lift his arm but had trouble pushing a plow or lifting a sack of grain. The younger nephew, Joseph, had fired a cannon so many times he lost the better part of his hearing. He had a ringing in his ears, and his face was pockmarked from the blowback. He was constantly on guard, scanning the surroundings for dangers he could not hear.

On the road, they told us the stories of Dooly County, including the horror of the prison just over the county line. Daniel said, "Andersonville marked the soul of everyone it touched." He told us about Louise's brother Sam Marsh. Sam had joined the local militia. Daniel said, "When Andersonville opened, Sam was assigned a detail that involved bringing food to the prison. He was appalled at the savage behavior starvation can cause. When he complained, he was assigned to a new detail.

"At first, it was presented as a promotion, a reward for his marksmanship. There was a border around the prison called 'no-man's land.' Sam was to walk the crosswalk and shoot any prisoner who crossed the line into the forbidden space. The corporal that trained him told him, 'a kill shot is kindest.'

"Sam had terrible nightmares. He woke up in terror, screaming for them not to go. He got to where he could spot them thinking about it. He would pray and silently beg them, but the terrible conditions made some so hopeless, they went."

Sam slowly lost contact with the world. He drowned in the Flint River a few months after Lee surrendered. His death was listed as an accident, but we could tell Mary Alice had her doubts. Mary Alice and the girls were lucky enough to sell their land. They moved in with Sam and Louise's mother, Rachel Marsh. Their father, Simon, had died early in the war. Now the two widows would be able to help each other.

Atlanta was in a fever of reconstruction, but the rest of Georgia was still reeling from the war, homes and barns burned, orchards cut, animals stolen or destroyed. The Andrews' farm had a soft roll of a hill that Carrie's grandfather had crowned with apple trees. The rows were straight and the spring blossoms must have been a sight to see. The Union troops had cut the trees for firewood, burned the barn, and taken the animals, but they had used the house as shelter and failed to burn it.

When we arrived, Milton was still rail thin. He always ate alone, and he did not speak. We sat together for days without a word on his part. He held his infant son and played silent games with the older boy, but did not talk. Carrie looked tired. She had her hands full, caring for Milton, her father, a young son, and now a new baby. The night before we left, Thomas waited till Carrie was upstairs with the children, then he gave Milton the bank note.

He also told Milton that Archie Moore had come home. Thomas brought a message from Archie. "Roscoe tried to make good on his promise."

Milton said his first and only word. "Hell."

It was just a whisper, but Thomas and I heard it loud and clear. It had many meanings but we were certain that if Archie was back in Wakulla, Roscoe was in hell.

In the morning, Thomas, his nephews, and I accompanied Milton to the bank. When the funds were deposited, we said farewell. Thomas and I hugged Milton as long as we could. We rode in silence that first day.

We worked our way home, staying the first night in Dooly, the second near Albany, and the third in Thomasville to see the farmer who had brought Thomas home. Joe Hanson had had a stroke and was not doing well. His wife, Anna, had suffered the loss of two sons; she was almost hysterical about Joe. We used the last of our travel money to put ham in their smokehouse and grits and coffee in the kitchen. By the time we got to the Florida line, we were both feeling the weight of the suffering around us.

We rode straight to get Louise. Not having the security Dooly had given her, Louise had stayed with our closest friends and nearest neighbor, Doc Gregory and his wife Lily.

Lily trained as a teacher but stayed home with her own small children. Both women helped Doc Gregory with patients when he needed them. After Doc watched Louise care for Thomas, he had asked her to help him on his rounds. Doc said she had a calming effect on his patients.

Louise could still soothe a tearful baby or make them smile. She was a comfort to the sick and an angel to the dying. The first time Doc asked Louise to help with a baby, she had blushed. "I wouldn't be much help. I've never had a baby."

Doc said, "I haven't either."

As Louise helped the expectant mother, she told the story.

The woman laughed so hard, Doc said, "The baby was born with a smile."

As we rode up, Louise ran to greet us. There was no hurry to revisit what we had seen and heard. We told the stories slowly.

36 Jo Nell

The storm that demolished the saltworks was the only devastating storm to hit us during the war. After that, it was as if the Gulf had saved them up and hit us steady for the next few years. Tropical storms hit Wakulla County in October 1867 and again in October 1868. The water got high from all of the rains. Roads washed out and most of the fields were too wet to plant. The cotton crop was devastated and the gin quiet. The downed trees were the only good that came from the storms. Jim and I were trying to plan for our sawmill. We still cut the trees off fences or roofs and stacked firewood for our neighbors, but we kept some of the lumber for our mill.

I loved my time with Jim in Panacea. His sister, Jo Nell, was always nice to be around, but it wasn't until she gave me the puppy that I fell in love with her.

I was still moping around about losing Dooly when she brought me the puppy, a female bulldog, white with a black eye and a black patch at the top of her tail. She looked just like a small Dooly. When Jo Nell gave her to me, she apologized. "I looked for a male, Henry, but she was all I could find." By the end of the day, I was in love with them both.

Jim had a big laugh. Later, he told me, "I sure am glad Jo Nell finally found that puppy. She's been looking for months and searched at least three counties." Jo Nell named the puppy, Daisy.

Jim saw how I looked at Daisy and Jo Nell. He decided we needed a pact. We made a promise. We would open the sawmill before we would marry. Jo Nell didn't speak to Jim for a least a month.

The storms provided lumber for the sawmill and, I have to admit, Jo Nell gave me incentive to get the mill operational. Jim and I worked long hours, using pulleys and mules to set the huge beams that would be the framework for the mill. We ordered parts from as far away as New Orleans and Key West. We milled our first tree in January 1870. Jo Nell and I set our wedding date for the first Saturday in February.

The night before the ceremony, Thomas came to talk. "Henry, you have always made me proud of you," he said. "You have been a good son in every way. I have no doubt you will be a good husband. Jo Nell is going to make a wonderful wife. Louise and I love you and wish you both all the best."

I never realized what a hard decision Thomas had made when he married Louise. If he ever had regret, he didn't show it. I hoped Jo Nell and I would always have the kind of love he and Louise shared.

Our wedding was at the little church the Hill family attended, at least Mrs. Hill and the children. It was a small wooden building with a cemetery that overlooked a saltmarsh. The cemetery was surrounded by a small wall made from limerock. Fred Hill was buried in the cemetery. Jo Nell's mom thought it was nice that Fred would be close.

We were married at eleven o'clock in the morning on a clear, winter day. Jo Nell is tall with long, dark hair and big doe eyes. The day of the wedding she never looked more beautiful. Her mother and her aunts made her dress. Small beads that looked like pearls were sown around the neckline. She carried a bouquet made from Johnny jump-ups tied with a piece of the material they used to make her dress. To me, it looked like she had come out of a dream.

Jim walked Jo Nell down the aisle then came to my side. Their sister, Mary Lynn, stood next to Jo Nell. The Duncan boys helped seat our guests. The little church overflowed with friends and neighbors.

I can close my eyes and still see everything about that day, still smell the salt air. After the ceremony, I walked Jo Nell out of the church to visit our other guests. Saltmarshes team with life, and when we exited the church, an osprey flew overhead, screeching his approval. A dozen mullet jumped out of the water to catch a glimpse of my bride.

The Gulf coast is the winter home of hundreds of bird species. Red-wing blackbirds, herons, egrets, kingfishers, pelicans, gulls, and ducks of every shape and color joined the celebration. The chatter of the birds provided a symphony of sound. A saltmarsh has a beauty that can never be captured by an artist's canvas. There is constant motion in a saltmarsh. The sea oats and grasses sway gracefully with the ocean breeze. The tides rise and fall. The abundant wildlife hunt for food or try to avoid becoming food. Together, they provide an ever-changing beauty. The sun, usually our enemy, was welcome on that cool day.

Tables full of food were set up in the churchyard. Most all the little church's parishioners were fishermen. We had every delight the Gulf could offer for our feast.

Our wagon was loaded down with gifts from our guests. It seemed that all of the families I had helped through those hard times brought us gifts. Some were small, a sack of onions or greens. Others were so lovely they took our breath away.

Martha Duncan had arranged a quilting bee for the families that I had cut wood for during the war. The ladies gave us a beautiful quilt. Each family had designed a block using a different wildflower design, giving the quilt the look of a bouquet. It was the prettiest quilt we had ever seen. Jo Nell's uncle carved a magnificent bowl out of a piece of driftwood, and Mrs. Walker gave us a real silver pitcher that had belonged to her mother. She thought Molly would want me to have it.

Lily Gregory brought her niece with them. Caroline also trained as a teacher in Tallahassee. She came to Wakulla to help her aunt with the family's latest addition. Caroline had big, blue eyes that pulled you in with the intelligence behind them. Jim immediately fell in love, even though he and Caroline were kind of opposite. Jim had skipped school to fish every chance he got, while Caroline had gone to college. Jim had his father's size. His shoulders just barely fit through most doorways. Caroline could slip through a crack.

I asked Jim, "You going to open the mill this week?"

Jim looked back at Caroline and answered, "No, I think I'll wait on you. I need the time at my house. The porch needs some work, and I have been wanting to straighten those shutters."

As we left the churchyard, a final visitor stopped us—the boy from the woods. His mother had call him "Bug." His hat in his hand, he flagged us to stop. "Mr. Henry, Missus, you probably don't remember me." He smiled before adding, "My family sure does remember you. My mama wanted me to be certain you got these pies." He handed me two sweet potato pies, neatly wrapped in a piece of gingham and tied with a string made into a bow.

Life gave me one more gift that day, although I didn't recognize it at the time. Friendship is one of life's greatest gifts. Bug and I would go on to work together and laugh together at the sawmill. We would count on each other for many years.

Within a year of our wedding, Jo Nell and I stood for Jim and Caroline at the same little church in the saltmarsh.

37 The Capitol Steps

Thomas had first been invited to attend the Democratic State Convention after he attended the rally at the Augusts' All Seasons Plantation in 1860. It had given him his first exposure to politics. He was invited back every year after that.

During the war, he had guarded the men who made decisions for the state. So many had died for the decisions these men made.

As a guard, Thomas was credited with foiling an assassination plot that turned out to be a wronged husband looking for revenge. He was ashamed he had guarded meetings and parties at the Capitol. He would never equal the sacrifice of others, but he could honor them by using what he had learned.

The year 1871 was especially wet. We had two tropical storms in two months, one in August and one in September. The water was high and the roads so wet, even the strongest mules couldn't drag logs to the mill. The cotton crop was damaged, along with most all of the other crops. The cotton gin was idle and so was our sawmill. Jim and I spent our time fishing and Thomas spent his time on politics.

Thomas was asked to run for office in 1872. If elected, he would serve as the State Representative for Wakulla County. Thomas told me, "The violence had devastating consequences. It is time to give our voices and our votes a chance."

Thomas was elected in a landslide. The Democratic candidate was always favored after the war, but Wakulla men went out of their way to vote for Thomas. He told me I won most of his votes with the chores I did for the families left behind and Louise had won the rest for her work with Doc Gregory.

Thomas bought a new buggy to take Louise to Tallahassee. Chief and I rode next to them. The water was still high and the roads poor. Louise had to lift her skirts in the buggy. Chief and I had to swim every now and then. We followed the Plank Road until it crossed the Old St. Augustine Road. We took the Old St. Augustine Road to the Capital. Louise and I had never been to Tallahassee before we arrived for the session.

As we approached the Capitol, our excitement grew. It had been built in 1845. Although the building was still brick in 1873, it had huge columns and was the most beautiful building I had ever seen. Live oaks and several magnolias surrounded the structure. Two Mountain Howitzers, cannons from the war, were at the bottom of the east stairs.

Thomas took us inside to see the floors as smooth as mirrors and the stairway wide enough for five people at once. We saw the chamber where he would work. We were thrilled by the grandeur.

After our tour, we went to a boarding house overlooking a small park. We were just up the street from the city cemetery. Princess Murat, the one who fired the cannon marking Florida's secession from the Union, had been buried there a few years earlier.

The State Capitol, 1845
Photo courtesy of Florida State Archives

When we arrived, we had some time before the boarding house served dinner, so Thomas took us to Monroe Street to shop. We all had our Sunday best with us, but that was not near what we would need for the session and parties that accompanied it. Thomas and I bought new boots, and Louise purchased a navy blue taffeta dress with lace at the bodice. Louise was in her forties, but the dress still made her look like an angel.

When the Legislative session started in 1873, the Speaker of the House announced, "We have some new members with us today. Since we all want to get to know each other, we're going to ask them to say a few words to introduce themselves. We'll go in alphabetical order by county. Each man will have a few minutes; you get long winded, and I'm going to cut you off!" A titter of laughter spread through the house.

Thomas listened while each representative made his presentation. Most of the speeches started with an account of the speaker's family. They emphasized the generations they had called Florida home. They recited the many titles each of their family members had held and how significant their contributions had been. Thomas was the last of the new members. When it was time for Thomas to speak, there was chatter here and there. He stood quiet for a minute.

Thomas was one of the only men on the floor who had actually spent time behind a plow. He had adopted Florida with the same love he had given me.

Thomas said, "It is an honor to represent Wakulla County and to serve the great State of Florida. History will judge the contributions Florida has made and those not yet made. While Florida may have been misguided in her efforts, her record leaves little doubt about the fervor of her conviction. Florida has been described as 'small' and Wakulla only a rural county. They match Shakespeare's words when he said, 'Though she may be but little, she be fierce!' I intend to honor the sacrifice so many have made, and when I speak, it will be Wakulla's voice you hear."

Thomas sat down to a trickle of applause that built to a roar as members stood.

We had an exciting week. A number of representatives came by to say they enjoyed Thomas's speech and how they wanted to help the rural counties.

We attended our first legislative party later that week. It was just a few blocks from our rooming house. The weather was excellent so we decided to walk. We were enjoying a wonderful time when the "belles" arrived.

The belles were beautiful young women desperate for a man or, at least, for support. After the war, men were in short supply. Any man with all four limbs or his faculties was a prize. A swarm of local beauties attended the barbeque. I was one of the youngest men in the room. I had to tell at least a dozen of the young beauties that my wife and new son were visiting her mother. Louise stood next to Thomas, but that didn't stop some of the flirting.

Thomas and Louise never said a word that night, but it was a big joke at breakfast. The boarding house served breakfast to all the boarders and the table was full.

Thomas started, "Henry, you must be made of honey the way all those 'bees' were buzzing around you last night. There must have been at least ten circling at any time." He asked Louise, "How many did you count?"

Louise said she couldn't count. "I was too busy shooing them away from you." The table shook with laughter.

Wakulla County was suffering from four tropical storms in just a few years. Our garden was so damp the roots of Louise's vegetables rotted in the ground. Thomas wanted a bill to help the poor farmers that had bad years. A number of senators and representatives praised Thomas for his vision. They offered their advice and promised to support the bill when completed.

Many of our neighbors had lost their land. Others were barely hanging on. Thomas would explain, "I just want a simple pay-out to hold the families over and provide seed for the next crop. Don't want them to starve or lose their land."

His new friends at the Capitol invited him to parties and always had time to talk about making his bill a reality. They expressed sympathy for Wakulla and her neighboring counties hit by the Gulf storms.

Backroom agreements were made to trade votes. Thomas was expected to support their bills and they would pledge their votes to his project. Hands were shaken, and there were smiles all around. Then they asked for information they considered essential to the bill being presented. It would take time to gather the information, moving the bill back on the agenda. When the bill finally came to a vote, a few grand speeches were made about the needs of the small farmers, but the budget was already promised to other projects.

The session ended, but no action was taken. In September 1873, just a few months after the legislature adjourned, a storm nearly swept the town of St. Marks away. Thomas had nothing from the legislature to offer his neighbors.

Frustrated by the process, Thomas declined to run for re-election. Louise was glad. She had had enough of the boarding house and the belles.

Thomas went back to being a farmer. Louise went back to her garden. They both looked forward to spending time with my growing family.

38 The Constitution

Though Thomas did not run for re-election, he continued to attend the Democratic State Conventions. He still acted as if he had an unpaid debt. He frequently was asked to run for office but always declined until the Florida Constitution became an issue. He was approached at the Convention about a committee that was being appointed to write a new constitution for the state.

This seemed to be the opportunity Thomas had been looking for. Wounds from the war were still not healed. Demons haunted the night. There were so many unknowns, and fear is bred from the unknown. This would be a way to ease the fears for all.

Thomas was asked to run for senator. He was determined, he would not be "hoodwinked" again.

When the votes were counted in 1882, Wakulla had elected Thomas to the Senate. Thomas used part of his Senate salary to lease a house in Tallahassee. He wanted Louise to have a garden and a place for them to spend time together. Thomas hired Bug's parents, Nathan and Rose, to look after the farm, while he and Louise stayed in the Capital.

Thomas and Louise attended few parties and he promised few votes. What he did was work on the Constitution. He made sure there was protection for his neighbors. He said it was his "Magnum Opus." The Constitution would prohibit slavery and guarantee civil and political rights, leading Florida into a new century, a new age. I never saw him prouder.

I was at the signing of the new Constitution. Thomas paused and closed his eyes right before he signed. He told me, "I waited for heaven to take my hand."

Thomas declined to run for re-election. He had faced all the ghosts that haunted him and made peace with the past.

He came home to Wakulla.

39 Memories

The next few months were a happy time. Thomas had an ease about him I had not seen since before the war. Jo Nell and I had a growing family and the kind of happiness that had been missing for so long. But life is always changing.

The day we lost Louise, Thomas came in from the field and found her sitting by the garden. He smiled at the sight, a basket of vegetables at her feet. It only took a few seconds for sorrow to overwhelm him. Heaven had a new angel.

Thomas was lost without her. At night, he would sit and stare at the stars. In the morning, he worked his fields. He spent most of his afternoons sitting under the big live oak in the front yard, whittling toys for my children. He had learned to whittle from his father. It gave him a connection with his past, but time weighed heavy on Thomas without Louise. In 1889, he went back to the Florida Senate. In 1891, he was nominated for President *pro tem.* Thomas was elected unanimously. I wasn't there that day, but I have been told, the applause was thunderous.

At the end of the session, 1891, Thomas returned home to Wakulla County. Bug's parents continued to work for Thomas. Rose cooked and helped with the house and laundry. Nathan tended Louise's garden and helped with the cotton gin. Thomas attended church and spent time with my family over the next few years, but his loneliness showed, until Ella Watts started to attend our Sunday services.

Ella was the kind of beauty that could turn every head when she entered the room. She was a widow with four children and had a determination that would make any of the belles proud. It didn't take much to see she had her eye set on Thomas. Ella never called him Thomas. It was always, "Senator."

Thomas could give Ella the security she needed. She could give him the one thing Louise could not, the possibility of a child. They were married on May 28, 1897. The local newspaper said Thomas would be free of the "cussedness of bachelorhood." They also mentioned her age, half of his, and how the house would be filled with the "happy sound of children."

Nathan and Rose stayed to help Ella. Thomas and I never talked about his new wife. It was the children that seemed to make Thomas the happiest. My childhood loft had been empty for years; now it was filled with the happy sounds the newspaper had talked about. Thomas would read to them, filling their evenings with the tales of Gulliver's journeys and creating a chorus of giggles when he referred to the children as "Lilliputians."

Fishing became a kind of ritual. Thomas would pick a day and everyone would forget their chores. Thomas would pack up Ella's children and I would pack up mine. We would spend the day together baiting hooks, untangling lines, and settling the occasional arguments. Those were great days.

Within a year, Ella produced a fine son. I called Thomas "a sly old dog" at least fifty times.

Thomas passed away August 1, 1900. He was sixty-eight and had never regained his strength after the war. Doc Gregory said his lungs were scarred. He had been particularly short of breath the last few times we visited.

I woke well before daylight that morning and walked out on my porch. I watched a star shoot across the early morning sky and something inside me knew.

People came from as far as Jacksonville for his service. Senators and representatives spoke at his funeral, each saying how much he cared about his adopted state, Florida, especially his beloved Wakulla County. I knew it was true.

Later, I sat on my porch, listening to the sounds of the night and looking for the brightest stars. I made both a promise and a wish. I promised I would blend the stories of our lives as the night blends a chorus of voices into one song, and I wished for heaven to lend a hand.

Epilogue

Nature was kind to Ella, but fate was not. She would be widowed again, less than two years after Thomas's death. She would remarry, but the loss of so many husbands in such a short time took a toll on her. At the time of her death, she was a widow yet again, collecting the pension Thomas left her. There was little left of his land or money.

When Thomas had retired from the Senate, the *Florida Times-Union* wrote:

> February 6, 1889
>
> Swearingen, Thomas F. — Crawfordville, Wakulla County, Fifth Senatorial District, Democrat, farmer, Methodist, married, age 57. Senator Swearingen is a native of Georgia and was educated in the common schools of the county. In May, 1861, he entered the

Confederate service as First Lieutenant of Company D, Third Florida Regiment of infantry. He served in the regiment for a year and a half, but was obliged to secure a discharge on account of ill health and returned to his home. Regaining his strength he again entered the service, this time in Colonel G. W. Scott's battalion of cavalry, in which command he served until the close of the war. Returning home after being mustered out, he took up the occupation of a farmer. In 1872 he was elected a member of the Assembly, serving in the session of 1873 and 1874. He was chosen a State Senator in 1882 and was a member of the Constitutional Convention of 1885. Senator Swearingen has been a delegate of every Democratic State Convention since 1860 with the exception of the last one, at St. Augustine. It is needless to add that he has always been a Democrat.

To Learn More

The author used the following sources in her research for this story. Readers can learn more about daily life at the time of the Civil War from these websites and books.

Apalachicola Area Historical Society:
  http://www.apalachicolahistoricalsociety.org
  (*Special thanks for the image that appears in Chapter 6.*)

Chickasaw History:
  http://www.tolatsga.org/chick.html

Dooly County Board of Tax Assessors:
  http://www.qpublic.net/ga/dooly/
  (*Special thanks for the image that appears in Chapter 1.*)

Florida Department of State, Division of Library and Information Services: http://dos.myflorida.com/florida-facts/florida-history/the-capitol/. (*Special thanks for the image that appears in Chapter 37.*)

Florida Division of Historical Resources: http://dos.myflorida.com/historical/

Florida Historic Capitol Museum: http://www.flhistoriccapitol.gov/exhibits.cfm

Florida Memory, State Library and Archives of Florida: http://www.floridamemory.com (*Special thanks for the image that appears in Chapter 19.*)

George Pickett Videos: http://www.history.com/topics/american-civil-war/george-edward-pickett/videos/the-battle-of-gettysburg

Hawkins, Eleanor B. A Brief History. Jefferson, The Keystone County: http://www.jeffersoncountyfl.gov/p/history-culture. (*Special thanks for the image that appears in Chapter 27.*)

Hunt, Irene. *Across Five Aprils*. Berkley Jam, New York, 2002. Print

Keats, John. *The Human Seasons*: http://www.poetryfoundation.org/poem/173737.

Moore, Clarence L. *The Grits Eaters*. Father & Son Publishing, Inc., Tallahassee, Florida, 2011, 186 pages.

Shakespeare, William. *A Midsummer Night's Dream*, Act III: http://www.william-shakespeare.info/act3-script-text-midsummer-nights-dream.htm

Shofner, Jerrell H. *Daniel Ladd: Merchant Prince of Frontier Florida*. University Press of Florida, Gainesville, Florida, 1978, 180 pages.

Some Civil War Action, Wakulla County Florida.: http://www.littletownmart.com/fdh/st-marks_civil_war.htm. (*Special thanks for the image that appears in Chapter 7. Image credit to F.D. Howard*.)

State Archives of Florida, Florida Memory:
https://floridamemory.com/items/show/255307.
See more at:
https://www.floridamemory.com/items/show/2553
07#sthash.44venDLj.Kp7TCpYD.dpuf.
(*Special thanks for the image that appears in
Chapter 24. . Image credit to paymaster John J.
Pratt, U.S. steamer Stars and Stripes.*)

The Constitution of 1885, Florida Constitution
Revisions Commission:
http://www.law.fsu.edu/crc/conhist/1885con.html

The Treatment of Prisoners, Point Lookout.
Southern Historical Society Papers:
http://www.csa-dixie.com/csa/prisoners/t59a.htm

Wikipedia, Cotton gin:
http://en.wikipedia.org/wiki/Cotton_gin.

If you enjoyed reading
The Smallest Tadpole's War
in the
Land of Mysterious Waters,
you'll love the audiobook version,
now available in
the **Historical Fiction** section
at
Audible.com.

About the Author

Diane Swearingen attended Florida State University receiving a BS in Elementary Education in 1972, and an MS in Library and Information Services in 1995.

Diane worked in Leon County as a classroom teacher and a school media specialist, retiring in 2009 after thirty-six years. She published "POWER," a non-fiction reading comprehension strategy, in the *Florida Media Quarterly* in 2009 and continued to work as a reading consultant for Renaissance Learning, Inc. until 2012.

The Smallest Tadpole's War in the Land of Mysterious Waters began with family research and has been a labor of love. Diane lives in Tallahassee with her husband, Thomas, the great-grandson of Thomas Franklin Swearingen on whose life this story is based.